Jackie Womack

"Don't Trouble Yourself on My Account,"

she said stiffly.

"Oh, but I do," he began, pulling her to him.

She struggled in his arms but he held her firmly. "Why even try?" he asked. "You know this is what you want."

And, as his lips came down on hers, she had to admit he was right. All the emotions she had kept in check surged through her in one overwhelming wave. She wanted to give herself completely to the sweet mastery of his hands, his lips.

BRENNA DRUMMOND
has written a novel full of real people set in the beautiful wine country of California's Napa Valley. This is her first Silhouette Special Edition.

D1234817

Dear Reader,

Silhouette Special Editions are an exciting new line of contemporary romances from Silhouette Books. Special Editions are written specifically for our readers who want a story with heightened romantic tension.

Special Editions have all the elements you've enjoyed in Silhouette Romances and *more*. These stories concentrate on romance in a longer, more realistic and sophisticated way, and they feature greater sensual detail.

I hope you enjoy this book and all the wonderful romances from Silhouette. We welcome any suggestions or comments and invite you to write to us at the address below.

Karen Solem
Editor-in-Chief
Silhouette Books
P.O. Box 769
New York, N. Y. 10019

BRENNA DRUMMOND
Proud Vintage

Silhouette Special Edition
Published by Silhouette Books New York
America's Publisher of Contemporary Romance

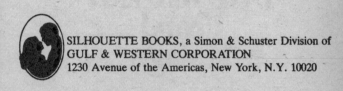
SILHOUETTE BOOKS, a Simon & Schuster Division of
GULF & WESTERN CORPORATION
1230 Avenue of the Americas, New York, N.Y. 10020

Copyright © 1982 by Brenna Drummond

Distributed by Pocket Books

All rights reserved, including the right to reproduce
this book or portions thereof in any form whatsoever.
For information address Silhouette Books, 1230
Avenue of the Americas, New York, N.Y. 10020

ISBN: 0-671-53542-0

First Silhouette Books printing August, 1982

10 9 8 7 6 5 4 3 2 1

All of the characters in this book are fictitious. Any resemblance to actual persons, living or dead, is purely coincidental.

Map by Tony Ferrara

SILHOUETTE, SILHOUETTE SPECIAL EDITION
and colophon are trademarks of Simon & Schuster.

America's Publisher of Contemporary Romance

Printed in the U.S.A.

Proud
Vintage

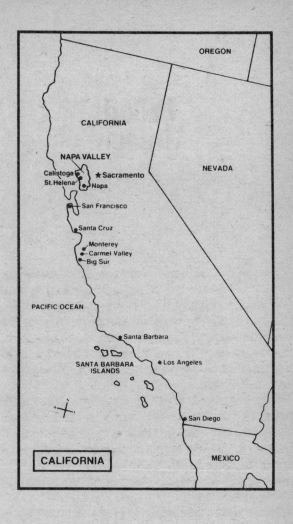

Chapter One

$\mathcal{K}$it was not sure what made her turn around. Perhaps it was the prickly feeling she got at the back of her neck or maybe some kind of sixth sense, but whatever it was she had the feeling that someone was staring at her. Curious, she turned her head and caught a glimpse of a tall dark figure standing at the end of the line.

There was no time to wonder about him because the line at the check-in counter suddenly moved forward and she found herself face to face with the ticket agent. She pulled the red-and-white ticket envelope from her purse and handed it to him. He glanced up at her and smiled.

"One ticket to San Francisco. Do you have

any luggage, Miss . . ."—he looked down at the name neatly typed in by the travel agent—". . . Carson?" he finished.

"Just this one case," she said lifting her suitcase onto the weigh-in table.

She watched him wrap a yellow ticket around the handle of her case and saw it disappear through metal doors with the other luggage.

"Your plane will board at Gate 10A in twenty minutes," he said, handing her back her ticket. "Have a nice flight."

"Thank you," she responded, flashing him a smile and putting the ticket envelope back into her shoulder-bag purse.

Twenty minutes. She had time to go and buy a magazine to read on the plane. She stepped aside as the line moved forward again, and out of the corner of her eye she caught a glimpse of the dark figure, who was now closer to her than before. He was still staring at her. She turned and walked briskly from the ticket counter, her shoulder-length honey-colored hair ruffling in the breeze she created by her rapid movement.

A tall slim girl with the figure of a fashion model, she had been stared at often enough in the past and, if she were forced to admit it, had enjoyed the attention. But that was before Tom. No, she would not think of him. That was over long ago. She would put him out of her mind.

She found the magazine rack and began

looking for something that would keep her occupied on the four-hour flight to San Francisco. She picked up one magazine after another and flipped through them, sizing up the articles that they contained. Then, out of the corner of her eye she saw an arm reach out next to her for a magazine. The arm was encased in a soft gray-and-brown tweed wool sleeve. She glanced idly over at the person standing next to her and found that it was the same man who had been staring at her from the back of the check-in line. His suit was not as dark as it appeared from a distance, but his hair was coal black.

Hastily she selected a magazine and walked over to the cashier to pay for it. It could be a coincidence of course, many passengers browsed through the magazine racks at the airport before boarding their planes. Or he could be following her. She paid for her magazine and rolled it into a cylinder in her hand before quickly walking toward Gate 10A.

It was a long walk and she tried to keep from turning around to see if the dark-haired figure was following her, but her curiosity got the best of her. Pretending to read the boarding signs of other departing planes, she stopped and swung her head around. He was following her. Not closely of course, but she could see his black hair in a crowd coming her way. Quickly she turned back.

This was ridiculous. He was probably taking the same plane that she was. She began walking toward Gate 10A again. Don't most people wait in line at the ticket counter, then often saunter into the magazine area before going down to the boarding area she reasoned. This was silly. She continued walking at a fast pace, however, her hair swinging out and then brushing the shoulders of her sea green jersey dress.

The plane had begun boarding when she reached the gate but having already selected her seat she felt no need to hurry. She reached into her purse and took out her ticket just as the boarding was announced again. The crowd surged forward at that moment and the ticket slipped from her grasp, fluttering onto the bright red carpet. As she stooped down to pick it up she was jostled by the passengers who were trying to move past her. For a brief moment she lost her balance and fell forward. Strong arms around her waist righted her.

"Thank you," she whispered breathlessly to her rescuer and found herself face to face with the same dark figure who had been staring at her from the back of the ticket line. Well over six-feet tall, he made an imposing sight in a soft gray-and-brown tweed suit which made a pleasing contrast against shiny black hair. But his eyes were what caught her attention. Instead of being dark they were a smoky gray.

"Let's move on," he said as the crowd swirled around them.

She quickly recovered her composure and

moved toward the boarding door. He followed her to the entrance of the plane and watched as she handed her boarding pass to the flight attendant and was directed to her seat. She quickly sat down then looked up expecting him to walk by toward his own seat, but to her surprise her rescuer lowered himself into the seat next to hers.

She unrolled her magazine and tried to pretend an interest in it as she heard the sharp click of his seat belt being fastened. She didn't look up.

"Don't you think you'd better do the same?" he asked in a deep voice.

She set her magazine on her lap and fastened her seat belt. True he had helped her in the boarding lounge but that did not mean she had to converse with him. This tall dark man was strangely disturbing. She decided to ignore him and read her magazine.

The plane was now loaded and the doors swung closed. It began backing out from its parking spot and making its way toward the runway. She did not look up. This was the part of the trip she dreaded.

"The take-off is one of the most exciting parts of the flight. You're going to miss it if you read your magazine," the voice beside her said.

Exasperated she turned toward him. "I appreciate your helping me in the boarding lounge but I fail to see how my missing the take-off is any concern of yours."

The gray eyes lit up and his lips curved into a sensual smile, making his face one of the most handsome she had seen in a long time.

"You have the greenest eyes I've ever seen," he said.

She lowered her eyes to the magazine. The nerve of him. Who did he think he was making a personal remark like that. Missing the take-off was just what she intended to do. She saw the flight attendant move down the aisle and heard the jet engines of the airplane roar into life.

She trembled slightly as a familiar fear seized her. Even though it had happened long ago when she was just a young child, the fact that her parents had been killed in a plane crash always caused her to feel nervous during the take-off. Her fingers gripped the magazine tightly. She would not look up. The airplane came to a stop. Startled she looked out of the window.

"We've got some other planes ahead of us today, so we're waiting our turn," her companion said calmly.

Despite her earlier resolve she looked over at him and shook her head. "I guess I'm a little nervous about this part of the trip," she admitted with a slight smile.

Before he could reply the airplane roared into life as the powerful jet engines drove it down the runway. She let the magazine slide from her lap to grab onto the armrests. She had succeeded in making herself unafraid of most aspects of flying except for the take-off. For some puzzling reason these few minutes caused her to almost quake with fear.

Suddenly she felt a large warm hand settle itself over her hand that rested on the middle armrest. The hand gave hers a gentle reassuring squeeze. She looked up into the smoky eyes and heard him say, "It's okay we're going to do fine."

She could scarcely breathe as the big jet lifted off the runway into the sky and the nose of the plane pushed upward into the clouds. A quick glance out of the window confirmed that the New York skyline was now lost in a milky swirl.

The hand resting on top of hers was removed. "We're up now and it will probably be smooth sailing to San Francisco. You can relax."

She looked up into a face that was inches from her own. "Thank you again," she murmured, trying to maintain her distance from the attractive face that looked down at her.

He nodded. She half expected him to try to make conversation but he reached out and pulled the airline magazine from the seat pocket in front of him and began turning the pages.

She took a deep breath. The fear had disappeared and she wasn't sure if the man on her left had anything to do with it or not. She retrieved her magazine and began thumbing through it. An article about a famous political figure and his family caught her eye and she relaxed. Soon she was engrossed in the magazine and forgot her earlier apprehension.

The drone of the plane's engines drowned out the background noises of crying children and the conversation of the other passengers. Before she knew it she was leaning her head back and closing her eyes. The noise of the plane was growing fainter and she was sinking into a dark, delicious oblivion.

She became aware of resting her head against something very solid but quite comfortable. Her eyelids fluttered open as she slowly awoke. She yawned and stretched her arms out and then jerked herself upright at what she saw. She had been leaning over in her seat with her head resting on the firm shoulder of her seatmate. She noted that he had removed his suit jacket and wore a snowy white shirt rolled back at the cuffs. Dark hairs peeked out where his wrists and forearms were exposed.

He saw that she was awake and a smile curved his lips. Deep grooves appeared at the sides of his mouth. He was truly the handsomest man she had ever seen. "Awake?" he asked casually.

"I don't even remember falling asleep," she said.

"It happens that way on airplanes. You sink back in the chair and the sound of the engines lulls you to sleep."

"You're right. That's just what happened. Thank you for the use of your shoulder."

"That's quite all right, Miss Green Eyes."

"Have I been asleep long?" she asked, trying to ignore his attempt at familiarity.

"You've been out almost an hour. They've already passed with the drink cart and are about to serve lunch, Miss Green Eyes," he said emphasizing the last three words.

Suddenly she felt silly at her reticence. Here was a perfectly charming man who had come to her rescue and allowed her the use of his shoulder and she was acting suspicious. Is that what Tom had taught her, to back away from all men? Well, this was one time that she was not going to do that.

She smiled at him and said, "You've rescued me from stampeding crowds and allowed me the kind use of your shoulder so I'd better tell you that my parents gave me a proper name."

"Oh, and what was that?" he asked, grinning broadly.

"Katherine Amanda Carson," she said, "but all my friends call me Kit."

This time his smile was brilliant and she felt a queer fluttery sensation as she looked at his attractive face.

"You mean . . . ?"

"That's right," she laughed. "Kit Carson, the famous scout, that's me. I've been amusing people for years."

"Adam Redmont," he said, extending his hand.

Again, the large, warm hand touched hers and she felt herself liking the feel of it encasing her own small slim one. She looked over at him and for a brief moment her eyes swept his square jaw before meeting his silvery eyes. She decided that he was in his early thirties, and from the absence of a ring, probably unmarried. He held her hand slightly longer than necessary before releasing it.

"Do you live in San Francisco?" she asked, to cover her unease at the feelings of attraction she felt for this perfect stranger.

"No, I'm going to the Bay Area on business," he replied. "Do you?"

She felt a stab of disappointment at his answer. "I live in the Napa Valley, which is about an hour and a half drive from the city."

Before they could converse further, the flight attendant approached with her lunch cart. They pulled the trays down from the seats in front of them and she set their lunch trays on them.

"I'll be right back with some coffee," she said, smiling at Adam.

Kit was aware of the amused grin on his face as she quickly looked away and unrolled her utensils from the napkin. He was probably used to beautiful women fawning over him, most handsome men were. Oh, well, it wasn't any of her business. She realized that she hadn't eaten anything at all before leaving for the airport that morning and was starving. She picked up a forkful of the green salad that accompanied her deliciously smelling entree of lasagna and began eating.

Adam was silent for a moment and then asked, "Do you live with your family?"

She thought it an odd question and wondered at the pause before he asked it. It was really none of his business and she oughtn't to be telling a complete stranger about herself.

"Yes," she said, and because she found his gray eyes boring straight into hers added, "That is, I live with my uncle, I don't have any other family."

"And what does Miss Kit Carson do in the Napa Valley?"

She knew she ought to break off the conversation right there and tell him it was none of his business. But there was something about him that compelled her to answer. She had vowed that after Tom she would trust no man, but at twenty-six she also knew that she would have a long lonely life ahead of her if she kept to that pledge. Anyway, what was a harmless bit of airplane conversation? It would help pass the time.

"My uncle and I run a small winery," she said, buttering a roll.

"A winery?"

She noticed a peculiar catch to his voice and, looking over at him, tried to see the look in his gray eyes that accompanied it. But he was breaking off a small slice of lasagna with his fork and so she caught nothing but his handsome profile.

"It's a small winery and the wine is sold locally. It's called Silverado, I don't suppose you've heard of it?"

"And what do you do at the winery?" he asked, grinning at her.

She was vaguely aware of the fact that he hadn't answered her question but his engaging grin and sheer masculine presence distracted her.

"My uncle owns the winery, actually, but I do a little bit of everything. I help out in the retail shop with the tours and tastings, I do the artwork for the advertising and I help him keep the books."

"Your uncle, is he an enologist?"

"You mean a wine maker? Yes, he trained as a chemist and worked for years at some of the big Napa Valley wineries. He finally decided to start his own. What do you do?"

She turned to look at him but he had just taken a bite of his salad and his head was turned away from her. She waited while he chewed his mouthful and it seemed to her she waited a lot longer than was necessary before the answer came.

"My family is in the investment business. I travel around the country looking for good investments for their money and for other people's money that we manage."

"Sounds interesting."

"It is."

She noticed that he had withdrawn slightly from the chatty conversational mode he had so quickly established. Perhaps he was growing bored with the whole conversation.

The flight attendant came back with the coffee and briskly filled Kit's cup with the steaming liquid. She paused longer than necessary over Adam, asking him if he took cream or sugar and smiling at him. Well, Kit thought, I can't blame her, he is a devastatingly attractive man. Anyway, just because he was sitting next to her it didn't mean that he was interested in her. He was probably passing the time with polite conversation the way she was doing.

But then he turned around to face her and lifted his coffee cup. "Ah, yes, where were we? You were telling me about your winery in the Napa Valley. Have you always lived there?"

"No, I haven't." She decided that she was giving him more information than the situation demanded and that she would be as closemouthed as he.

She sipped the coffee and raised her lashes to catch an amused grin on his face. Finally, her natural outgoing personality got the best of her and she burst out with, "Well, what's so funny?"

"You obviously have taken offense because I don't want to talk business, Miss Green-Eyed

Kitten. I'm using these four hours to relax after a very hectic few weeks, and I don't seem to be able to get interested in telling you anything about my work. Yours seems infinitely more fascinating to me right now."

His rueful grin made her instantly sorry she was suspicious. He was probably on the road a lot and the last thing he wanted to do was talk business. Momentarily she reflected on his choice of a name for her. Tom had always called her Katherine and her Uncle Matt used Kit, but here was a perfect stranger using a very familiar name and the strange thing about it was that she liked the sound of it very much.

"Okay, sorry," she said, "I don't mind telling you about the winery if you are really interested."

"Oh, but I am," he said turning his handsome face toward her.

She looked at the prominent nose and curving sensuous lips, then raised her eyes to his and found that he was regarding her seriously, almost expectantly. "Well, it's small by today's standards. We don't have a huge place at all. The story is that during the last century a Frenchman started it. He came to this country after having an argument with his family, who owned vineyards in France, and looked for an area in which to grow grapes. He found that the Napa Valley with its long hot summer was the perfect place. He had a winery built and caves carved out of a hillside to store the wine so it would be cool. Eventually, his vineyards grew and he started making wine."

"Don't tell me, then phylloxera came and he was ruined."

There was something about the way he said it that made her pause, it was almost as if he already knew the story. "You do know about the wine business," she said, half question, half statement.

"It's a hobby of mine," he added blandly.

She took the statement at face value. "The Frenchman left no heirs, and after phylloxera was controlled, prohibition came and the winery passed from one family to another. It fell into disrepair over the years but my uncle felt that he could rebuild it. So, when the opportunity to purchase it came along, he took the money he had saved from consulting for the large wineries and purchased the property."

What she didn't tell him was that things had grown so much more expensive than her uncle had imagined and he had to continually borrow money to keep the winery going. Now, it seemed with her unsuccessful attempts to interest eastern buyers in Silverado wine, the future of the winery was not at all bright.

They finished their coffee in silence and the trays were cleared away.

"You have a lot of responsibility, Kitten," he said softly.

She wondered why she was so moved by the

way he said her new nickname. It was almost as if he had known her before.

"Yes," she answered, "I do."

He stretched out his long legs and leaned back in his chair. "I've been up for the last twenty-four hours and right now I need a nap. Maybe I'll use your shoulder," he teased.

"Turnabout is fair play," she shot back before thinking about what she had said. She didn't want him to think she was an easy conquest.

But his head was already leaning over toward the aisle and his eyes were closing. Maybe it was just as well that he cut off the conversation. She was telling him entirely too much about herself and she was finding that she enjoyed his company too much for her own good. After all, Adam was a stranger whom she had just met. Hadn't she learned anything at all from what had happened?

She looked out the window at the clear blue sky that seemed to remain motionless as the big jet streaked through it. I haven't told him half the story, she thought, and it is good that he stopped me before I did. No one since Tom had caused her to let her guard down. She had vowed after her experiences with him that she would never do it again, but here she was telling a perfect stranger all about herself.

On the other hand she would probably never see him again, anyway, and after two years it felt good to relax in the company of an attractive man and, yes, she had to admit it, flirt a little. At least Tom had not crushed her natural good spirits forever.

Tom. What had made her think she was in love with him she still did not know. She supposed it was the fact that he was older and seemed so exciting to her at the time. She had known the Angelli family since she had come to live with her uncle when she was very young. They owned a large prosperous Napa Valley winery and their dark-haired daughter, Angie, became her best friend soon after they met and then introduced her to Johnny, her older brother. He was a quiet, serious person and Kit liked him but when she met Angie's other brother, Tom, she could not stop thinking about him.

He didn't notice her until she grew out of her pigtails and girlish clothes. Her slim body began to curve, her long legs became willowy and she began to fill out her sweaters and slacks with her graceful form. One day, home from college for the summer, she was over at the Angelli house visiting Angie when he roared up in his new foreign car. She'd given up believing that he would notice her, but as he bounded into the living room that day he stopped and asked to be introduced to Angie's new friend.

Kit remembered the two of them laughing and trying to pretend that she was a new friend, someone whom he had never met. But as he stepped closer, bringing his tall athletic body and baby blue eyes nearer to where she sat, he said, "You're Katherine Carson. God, I haven't seen you for years and look what's happened to you."

She had looked at the tall good-looking blond standing in front of her and had fallen in love with him on the spot.

She was working at the winery that summer and was involved with a group of tourists when he walked into the retail shop. One look and she knew that he had come to ask her out.

From that day on she was Tom's girl. They dated regularly and when she graduated from college he asked her to marry him. She agreed, of course, and the Angelli family was delighted.

For a brief period their marriage was everything she dreamed it would be until one day she discovered that her handsome blue-eyed husband had been going out with another woman. She was shocked and numbed by her discovery and felt that she had failed.

After brooding about it she confronted Tom. He laughed and said that she was just a child and though he had been amused with her for a while, it took a real woman to satisfy him. She packed her bags that day and went back to live with her uncle.

It was not until after she left that she heard about Tom's gambling and his debts and the fact that the woman he had been seeing was very rich. She supposed that he did not want to tell his family about his gambling and, for a while, even thought that he might come back to her, but he did not. Then she got angry that he had treated her like a baby and not told her about his problems and she went to see him, only to find that he had left the valley.

They lived apart for two years as she picked up the pieces of her life and put her education to work by helping her uncle in the winery. Tom's family was embarrassed and upset by his behavior and Angie, still her best friend, was furious with him. Then one night Kit received a phone call from Johnny telling her that Tom and his girlfriend had been killed in a flaming automobile accident in Las Vegas.

By that time she had lost whatever feeling for him she once had, but at the same time, she was deeply saddened by the waste of a life. She had her name legally changed back to Carson and plunged herself into her work, rarely going out. It was the financial affairs of Silverado Winery that finally brought her out of her self-imposed seclusion. She marshaled her knowledge of business and finance and began traveling around the country, trying to interest buyers in selling Silverado wine in their shops. Her uncle was busy looking for financing to help him pay the rising costs of running a winery and make needed repairs.

Kit was sad to have to admit that this trip to the east had been a failure. She had not been able to get commitments from any of the eastern buyers or wine exporters that she had talked to. She hoped her uncle had fared better with the financing.

A sudden movement to her left brought her out of her reverie and she turned to her seat companion. He was still asleep but his body was now leaning over in her direction. She looked at the sleeping face. It had a boyish quality to it and the lines around his eyes were softened as he slept.

She let her eyes wander down the length of his outstretched legs. His tweed slacks accentuated the muscled firmness of his thighs and long legs. The white shirt now rolled back to the elbows revealed muscular arms and broad shoulders. She wondered how he found time to exercise because, as she looked at the virile masculine body stretched out next to her, she noted that there was not an ounce of spare flesh on it.

His hands rested lightly on the armrests and, even in sleep, she could see that they were the hands of someone used to taking charge of a situation, just as they had during the take-off. Large, pulsing with life, they rested next to her and she wondered how they would feel on her body. Would they be as devastating as his hand had been enclosing hers?

She mentally shook off that kind of thinking and shifted her attention to his face. Despite the handsomeness of it, his face had a rugged quality. She supposed that if the square jaw and prominent nose were not in proportion to each other he would not have been nearly as good-looking. She remembered the smoky gray of his eyes, and as her gaze wandered to the dark brows and the coal blackness of his hair, she suddenly realized that his eyes were not closed in sleep anymore but were open and staring at her.

Chapter Two

*E*xamining the merchandise?" he asked with a wide grin.

Trapped, she became defensive. "In a way I was. I sketch, you see, and I thought you would make a good subject," she replied stiffly and turned back to her magazine. It was true, she did sketch and she supposed she could have been studying him for that reason. But deep down that lean muscular body brought out feelings that she hadn't felt for a long time.

"Don't get huffy, Miss Green-Eyed Kitten," he said softly, sitting upright in his chair. "I would like to have you . . . sketch me," he added with a deliberate pause.

She looked up from her magazine into the gray eyes and found that they were twinkling and the sensual mouth was smiling wickedly. She knew she was being teased.

She relaxed and tried to shake off the heaviness of her earlier thoughts and concentrate on Adam Redmont. Why not, since it was only until they landed in San Francisco and she would probably never see him again.

"I really do sketch. I was an art and business major in college and managed to learn advertising by combining the two. I helped Uncle Matt design the Silverado label and the brochure for the winery," she said earnestly, lifting her green eyes to his.

"It sounds as if you're devoted to both your uncle and the winery," he said gently.

She nodded. "I've lived in the Napa Valley since I was a child. When my parents died my uncle took me in to live with him. We lived in a small house in St. Helena until he purchased the winery and then we moved out of town into the house that was built next to it. I've lived there ever since."

She had deliberately left out the part about Tom and her disastrous marriage. She rarely shared that part of her life with anyone.

Adam was watching her intently. "Go on," he urged.

"Well, that's all there is to tell," she said self-consciously, embarrassed at the way his eyes studied her shoulder-length hair and pale skin. "Have you ever been to the Napa Valley?" she asked, trying to shift the subject from herself to him.

"Yes," he smiled, "I have. I come out to the Bay Area regularly on business and when I have time I visit the valley."

"We're going to show a movie now," the flight attendant said, breaking into their conversation. She handed each of them a plastic bag containing blue vinyl earphones.

Kit took hers reluctantly. She did not want the conversation to end. Adam had just begun to tell her about himself and she wanted to know more.

He took his earphones and with a rueful grin said, "Guess we'll have to postpone our conversation, Kitten."

He sounded as if he were genuinely disappointed, or maybe he was just being polite. She hoped her disappointment did not show. She was being very silly by becoming attracted to this perfect stranger anyway. To cover her embarrassment she fumbled with the plastic bag. He reached over to help her and his hand brushed hers. She felt the impact of his nearness and turned to look at him. His face was inches from her own as he tore open the bag and extracted the earphones. Then he turned to her.

He placed the earphones gently around her neck, his hands brushing her shoulders in feather light touches. She was unprepared for the feeling of intimacy she felt from this act and the crazy desire to be in his arms. She caught her breath at the intensity of the feelings that swept through her. She must be out of her mind.

From the front of the plane the screen was lowered and the plane's interior lights turned off. The first scenes of the movie flashed on the screen. Adam adjusted his own earphones and, finally, the two of them settled back to watch the film. It was a lighthearted comedy, one that she had not seen before.

A few moments went by before she realized that he had turned in his seat and was not watching the movie but was staring at her. She looked at him surprised. He reached out and clasped her hand in his. She was startled for a moment but the feel of him holding her hand was what she had wanted since the take-off. She looked at him and he gave her hand a gentle squeeze. Then she smiled to tell him yes, thinking all the while that it would be very hard to tell Adam Redmont no after this.

As the story on the screen unfolded, the movie captured their attention and before long they were chuckling at the exploits of the hero and the heroine. Occasionally Kit's glance would rest on their hands clasped together, her small one held gently in his. It was as if they were made to fit together, as if their bodies would fit together just as naturally.

She was shocked by her own thoughts. She was an adult sitting on an airplane with someone she had just met and they were holding hands as if they had been lovers for years. Sometimes her own recklessness surprised her. Even as a child she had followed her emotions instead of her uncle's advice.

"You are an impulsive child," Uncle Matt had once told her as she ran into the small house they shared to tell him about the tree she had just climbed and swung from Tarzan style.

She had asked him what that word meant and he told her that she did things without thinking them through. He told her he did not want her to stop having a good time but he also did not want to see her get hurt. She would always promise to be more careful and he would give her a quick hug and let her go back to her friends.

She was being impulsive now, she knew, holding hands with a stranger. She thought that Tom had stamped that trait right out of her forever. But she was wrong.

As if sensing her thoughts Adam turned to look at her. She returned his gaze and he leaned over to tell her something. Pushing her earphone aside with a gentle movement, he started to whisper in her ear just as the movie ended and the lights came on.

"I'm not in the habit of holding hands with women I meet on airplanes if that's what you're thinking," he said.

He released her hand and she pulled the earphones away from her neck. "Nor am I in the habit of allowing it," she said softly.

They remained staring at each other, an unspoken pleasure lingering between them. The flight attendant came by to retrieve the earphones and Adam turned away to hand them to her.

Kit began to feel that they were becoming too serious all of a sudden. To give herself a break from Adam Redmont's magnetic attraction, she unlatched her seat belt and stood up. With her purse tucked under her arm she stepped over his feet. "Excuse me," she said and then walked up the aisle to the restroom.

Once inside the cubicle she splashed cold water on her face and carefully blotted up the moisture with a paper towel. She smoothed the soft jersey dress and brushed her hair. She realized that she was acting like a giddy schoolgirl, but there was something both compelling and exciting about this handsome man, something that made her want to get to know him better and hope that she would have the chance.

She reapplied her lipstick, took one final glance at herself in the mirror and was briefly surprised at the wide-eyed look in her green eyes. She was no schoolgirl and Adam was nothing if not a man of the world. He probably had a string of women all over the country, yet there was her impulsive streak telling her to take the risk. Her uncle had been right in the past, she had gotten hurt, but she could not stop herself this time, nor, if she were completely honest with herself, did she want to.

Making her way back down the aisle she was conscious of his eyes on her. It was as if they were smoky magnets and she was being drawn to them and could not stop herself. Once she got closer she saw that they were examining her carefully, moving from the honey blond hair lying smoothly on her shoulders, pausing to rest at the swell of her breasts outlined by the thin jersey dress and then continuing to move down the length of her five foot seven inch frame to her hips and her slim legs.

She stepped over his feet on the way to her seat and asked impishly, "Examining the merchandise?"

"What do you think?" he asked without blinking an eyelash nor seeming to be the least bit embarrassed at being caught staring so blatantly at her.

At that moment the airplane dipped and she swayed, trapped between his knees and the seat in front of him. Strong hands shot out and gripped her waist, steadying her.

His touch excited her. "Thanks," she said, "I don't want to fall into your lap."

"I wouldn't mind having a purring kitten in my lap," he said softly. "You do know how to purr? or will I have to teach you?"

He smiled that glorious sensual smile and his hand slid caressingly from her waist to lightly graze her hips as she quickly stepped over his feet and sat down, ignoring the question. Before she could move he leaned over and drew the seat belt around her. One side of the belt had become scrunched under her and his hand reached between her hip and the cushioned seat to free it. It was an intimate gesture and while he was leaning over she smelled the faint aroma of aftershave and noticed that the crisp black hair curled slightly at the back of his neck. He succeeded in freeing the seat belt then withdrew his hand to secure the belt in front of her. An ache to have those strong, sure hands grab hold of her suddenly overwhelmed her. Before she could hide the feeling, he looked at her and saw what she did not want him to see.

He leaned over and whispered, "Someday, my green-eyed Kitten, we won't be on an airplane and I will teach you to purr."

At that moment the plane began bumping up and down as if they were on a roller coaster ride. Kit tensed in her seat as the captain's voice came over the loudspeaker.

"Sorry, folks, we have a little turbulence over the Sierra Nevadas, so fasten your seat belts and try to relax. We'll soon be out of it."

Adam saw her sitting stiffly in her seat. "He's right, Kitten, these things happen all the time. Nothing to worry about," he said.

But Kit could not rid herself of the nameless fear that tightened her chest and made her tense with anxiety. The plane shook and dropped slightly and then began buffeting in the wind. She looked over at Adam and found he was relaxed and smiling as usual. One look at her grim expression and he reached out and picked up her hand and held it firmly in his.

As quickly as it came the turbulence stopped and the plane resumed its smooth course. Kit let out her breath in a sigh of relief. He continued holding her hand in his firm grip.

"Why so nervous, Kitten? You've been flying before."

At first she wasn't going to tell him. She didn't know why she blurted it out the way she did. "My parents were killed in an airplane crash when I was very young. I don't remember it at all but sometimes when I'm flying I get a strange panicky sensation. It's silly, I know. They weren't even flying commercially, I found out much later. They had gone up in a private plane and got caught in a storm."

His grasp on her hand tightened for a fraction of a second. "Sorry to rake up old memories. I love flying. I'm a pilot myself."

"You mean you have your own airplane?"

He laughed. "No, I'm not that kind of pilot. I'm a sailplane pilot. You asked if I'd been to the Napa Valley and the answer is yes. When I'm in the Bay Area I frequently take time to go to Calistoga and go soaring."

"A sailplane pilot, I never would have guessed."

"Why do you say that?"

"Oh, I don't know. I've seen the sailplanes riding the winds that hug the ridges of the valley and I suppose it would be fun to try it. But you're so . . ." she stopped, trying to find the right word.

"Macho," he supplied, with a teasing glint in his eyes.

"And conceited," she laughed. The unease and fear she had felt during the air turbulence had disappeared. Adam continued to hold her hand and the heady feeling of exitement continued to ignite a fiery warmth deep within her.

"Why don't I take you soaring with me the next time I come out to Calistoga?"

"Why . . . yes, I would like that very much."

"Good."

The loudspeaker crackled and the flight attendant's voice came on. "We'll be landing soon at the San Francisco International Airport. Please make sure that your hand-held luggage is stowed beneath your seat, extinguish all cigarettes and bring your chair to its full upright position. The captain has turned on the 'fasten seat belt' sign."

The airplane banked for a turn and Kit looked out her window and saw the Golden Gate Bridge gleaming in the sunlight and the clear blue waters of San Francisco Bay.

"It's good to be back," she said softly, almost to herself.

But Adam heard her. "Have you been gone long?" he asked.

"No, not really," she said turning from the side window to look at him. "I guess I just miss my home and my uncle and the smell of the grapes."

A strange look passed over his face but before she could figure out what it was, he said, "Looks like we're coming in for a landing now."

She had the oddest feeling that he had spoken merely to cover up some other kind of emotion that he was feeling and did not want her to recognize.

The landing was smooth as the jet skimmed over the runway then set down so gently that some of the passengers in the plane broke into applause. Kit watched the landscape whizzing by as the plane began to slow down. She turned in her seat to look at Adam while he held up her hand in a triumphant gesture as if to say, we won.

She took a deep breath. "This is the first time I've enjoyed the landing."

He leaned over and said, "This is the first time I've enjoyed the flight."

Kit gave him a shy smile. She wondered what would happen when the flight ended. Would he ask to see her again? How long would he be staying in the Bay Area? Her impulse was to blurt out an invitation for him to come and visit the winery but something made her hesitate. Maybe after all these years she was finally taking her uncle's advice and being sensible.

The plane slowed down and taxied to the unloading area. The engines were shut off and people began unlatching their seat belts and standing up. Adam released her hand to unfasten his own seat belt. She did likewise, then reached under the seat in front of her to pull her purse and magazine out. Passengers began moving down the aisle toward the door of the plane.

Adam stood up, retrieved his jacket from the overhead rack and tossed it casually over his arm. Kit secured her purse on her shoulder and grasped the magazine in her hand. She stood up and he let her move in front of him into the line of people waiting to exit the plane.

As they slowly inched toward the door she kept waiting for him to ask her when he could see her again but he remained silent. Well, she thought, maybe he'll ask me when we get to the lobby away from all these people. He had invited her for a sailplane ride hadn't he? That meant he wanted to see her again. She would like him to meet her uncle and see the winery. She would extend the invitation when they got to the lobby.

"Goodbye, goodbye," the flight attendant said as each passenger passed her.

Kit nodded and stepped from the plane onto the unloading ramp that had been wheeled into place. It was nice not having to climb down the long stairway that was usually rolled up to the plane. The unloading ramp was a long carpet-covered hallway that allowed passengers to walk directly from the plane to the lobby of the airport.

He was behind her, she knew, but there were so many passengers moving down the narrow hallway that she dared not stop or turn around to say anything to him. No, that would have to wait until they got out of the crush of people and reached the lobby.

As they approached the doorway she could see crowds of people lined up ready to greet the arriving passengers. She hardly glanced at them because she knew that her uncle would not be one of them. She and her uncle had an agreement about meeting planes. They never parked and went into the airport; instead, they called to make sure that the plane would arrive on time and then drove up to the arrival area opposite the baggage-claim turntables and waited for the arriving passengers to come out the doorway. They had worked it out to allow time for the passenger claiming luggage and usually never had to wait in the loading zone for more than five minutes.

"Adam, Adam, over here," a female voice shouted as she entered the arrival area of the airport.

Kit looked over to see a woman, about her age, dressed in a chic maroon-colored knit suit waving and smiling. She was shorter than Kit. But her attire and chic haircut said she was a lot more sophisticated. When she finally caught Adam's attention, she stepped forward and slid her hands around his neck.

"Darling, your plane was right on time. I'm so glad to see you."

Kit could feel a sick ache in the pit of her stomach as she watched the man who had suddenly come to mean a great deal to her hold someone else in his arms. She knew she had to get away from the scene as quickly as possible. She kept right on walking, pulled along by the crowd, to the escalator.

It had been a pleasant four hours for him that was all, a diversion for a handsome man trapped on an airplane. She was a fool to have thought for one moment that their meeting and all of the hand holding meant anything else. But then, she had always been a fool where men were concerned. She seemed to attract the handsome ones without any scruples. They picked her up and then cast her aside like driftwood on the beach. Well, she had learned her lesson once and for all. She was twenty-six and she would remain unattached until she was eighty-six. Angry tears started to form in the corners of her eyes as she rode the escalator to the baggage-claim area.

She held herself in rigid control and positioned herself in front of the turntable that would spit out the luggage from the arriving jetliner. She would not cry. She would not shed one tear over the foolish way she had behaved during the last four hours. She would wait for her suitcase and leave the airport as quickly as possible. With luck, he would be trapped upstairs for a while and she would never have to set eyes on him again. At least this lesson was not as costly as the one she had learned with Tom.

More passengers came to stand next to her, waiting for the luggage to be spewed out onto the stainless steel apron that surrounded the turntable. She darted a quick glance over her shoulder but caught no sight of a tall black-haired man.

Hurry up, she silently begged the turntable. *Hurry up so I'll never have to see him again*. As if in direct answer to her silent prayer, the turntable began to move and the first pieces of luggage appeared at the top of the ramp and slowly slipped downward to the rim of the apron.

She hoped that because she had boarded her airplane quite late, her luggage would be among the first to be unloaded and she was right. With a sigh of relief she saw her suitcase appear at the top of the ramp then slide to rest right in front of her.

She reached over and picked it up. She would not bother to get any help with it. She would carry it herself to the door. Anything, to get out of there as fast as possible. An official stopped her and she had to retrieve her claim check from her purse and match the number of the ticket wrapped around the handle of her suitcase.

Suddenly she caught sight of the tall dark-haired figure riding down the escalator. She hurriedly picked up her bag and made for the doorway. A car braked at the sidewalk and a tall, slim, blond man got out, slamming the door behind him.

"Kit!"

"Johnny," she said, setting down the suitcase and wrapping her arms around his neck in a quick hug. "What are you doing here? Is anything wrong with Uncle Matt?"

"Not a thing except that he's having trouble with some of the equipment and couldn't leave. He called and asked me to pick you up and of course I told him I would. Sorry I'm late."

"You're just in time," she said.

He put her suitcase into the trunk of his car and as he opened the car door for her she glanced to her right into the luggage area of the terminal. Through the glass she could see the tall dark figure and a shorter one in a maroon suit striding toward the door.

Quickly she got into the car. Johnny closed her door and went around to the driver's side and got in. A policeman motioned for them to move out of the loading zone, and Kit breathed a sigh of relief when Johnny started the motor and slowly eased the car away from the curb.

She forced herself not to look back as the car moved into the traffic stream and sped away from the airport. For a few moments an ache engulfed her as she replayed in her mind Adam holding the girl in the maroon suit in his arms.

Then she sighed, straightened her shoulders, took a deep breath and put him out of her mind.

Chapter Three

"How was the trip, Kit?" Johnny asked, breaking the silence of the ride.

"Oh, you know how airplane rides are, long and tiresome," she replied.

"That was not the part of the trip I meant. How did your selling campaign go?"

Relieved, she began telling him about her unsuccessful attempts to interest any of the buyers she had talked to in Silverado wine. He asked her questions in his quiet serious manner, and they soon became engrossed in talking about the wine business.

The Golden Gate Bridge came into view and Kit stopped talking for a moment to stare at the sailboats dotting the bay. It was a clear, glorious summer day and she could see Angel

Island sitting in the blue bay waters. As they crossed the bridge she glanced at the joggers and walkers making their way across the span. Then she turned her attention back to Johnny.

"How's Angie?" she asked.

"I don't know if I should be telling you this," he said, smiling, "but I will anyway. She's pregnant."

"Oh, I bet she and Ray are thrilled," Kit replied.

"They are but my parents are even more delighted."

Angie, her best friend, already happily married and now with a child on the way. If she were forced to admit it she would say that having a happy marriage and a family had once been very important to her. Now, she realized that that would never happen. No, Tom had changed that. She would work in the winery helping her uncle for as long as they were able to hold on and if worse came to worse she would try to get a second job in an advertising agency and use her income to keep the winery going.

She looked over at Johnny and for a moment allowed herself to wonder what would have happened if she had married him instead of his older brother. Quiet, serious Johnny had also noticed her when she came home from college to visit Angie but unlike Tom had kept to the background and never asked her out. He worked hard and long in the Angelli winery that he would inherit one day. Since Tom's death they had become good friends. She hoped that he did not expect anything more than friendship because that was all she was capable of giving.

They crossed the bridge, leaving the city behind, and headed inland toward the Napa Valley. The weather became warmer and Kit rolled down the car window to feel the warm air blowing on her face. She needed to breathe in the smell of the grapes growing and the fresh clean air of the valley.

It was only late June and the grapes were still young on the vines. Many said it was impossible to smell them but Kit insisted to all the tourists who stopped at the winery at this time of year that she could. She told them that they would, too, after living in the valley a while.

Late September was the time that they agreed with her. Then, the aroma was a heady one because the crushing had begun and the whole valley would be filled with the intoxicating fragrance of the harvest.

They drove in silence until they turned onto the Wine Road, the nickname given to Highway 29 by some because it leads to the Napa Valley where grape growing and wine making are the major industries.

She breathed in the first faint smell of the grapes wafting through the open window.

"Oh, it's good to be back, Johnny."

"I've missed you, Kit," he said quietly.

"Have you? I've only been gone for two weeks."

"You know what I mean."

"Johnny, I . . ."

"Kit, you don't have to say anything or explain how you feel toward me. I was merely telling you that I missed you and that I'm here if you need me."

He took one hand off the steering wheel to gently squeeze her hand resting on the seat beside him. For one moment the feeling was almost too much to bear. His gentle squeeze was so unlike the warm hand that had held hers in its firm grip on the airplane that she almost cried out in disappointment.

"Thank you, Johnny. You and Angie are my dearest friends."

He said nothing for a moment and then, "I'll be content with that for now."

She barely heard him because now they were approaching the vineyards and she was wondering if the summer sun was going to be hot enough and shine long enough to make a high sugar content in the grapes and produce a good vintage.

They drove through St. Helena, the small town where she had spent many of her childhood years. A flag flew atop the tallest building on the main street and people sat in the park picnicking and sunbathing on the lawn. There was a lot of traffic on this warm summer day so that their drive through town was a slow one. Finally, they sped along the highway, as fast as the traffic would allow, until they came to a small sign, exquisitely lettered by Kit herself, proclaiming, "Silverado Winery, tours by appointment only."

Next to it was a mailbox with "Carson" lettered across it. He turned the car onto the road next to the sign to begin the drive up Whistler Mountain. It was a steep road, deeply rutted, and they bounced up and down even in Johnny's comfortable Chrysler.

Kit never minded the road, they couldn't afford to have it paved and she had gotten used to the way it was long ago. She craned her eyes for a glimpse of the house through the trees. Redwood, buckeye and madrone provided a thick cover until they neared the top and the trees gave way to a gravel driveway, a garden planted with fruit trees and a profusion of sun-loving flowers. As he braked to a stop her eyes scanned the golden yellow dahlias, zinnias and bright orange chrysanthemums.

So, she thought as Johnny opened the door for her, Uncle Matt has done some watering while I was away. She had made him promise to, telling him that if she came back and found all of her flowers dead she would never let him forget it. He had replied wryly, "I'm sure of that."

Now, savoring every moment that it took for Johnny to get her suitcase out of the trunk, she stared at the house. It was a magnificent Victorian house built over a smaller one-story house owned by an earlier settler of the valley. The Frenchman who founded the winery, to his credit, had saved the smooth-stoned old house by building his Victorian over it so that it became the first story of a three-storied house. To soften the gable roof he had added a veranda that ran the length of the second story and rested on four white pillars, spaced evenly along the front.

Later, another owner had had part of the veranda glassed in so that it was possible to sit out and watch the stars on the coolest of nights. The winery ran along the other side of the road. The tall redwood barnlike structure contained the stainless steel tanks used to hold the fermenting juice of the grapes. Against the mountain, caves, carved out of stone in the beginning of the century, and now braced by reinforced steel, were concealed by a heavy wooden door. There the redwood and oak barrels that held the wine while it aged were kept in a natural cooler.

"Are you okay?" Johnny asked, breaking into her thoughts.

"Of course, silly. I've missed this place during the last few weeks and I'm just enjoying the feeling of coming home."

Her Uncle Matt appeared at the side of the house. He looked as if he had just finished working on something because he was wiping his hands with a rag that he quickly stuck in the back pocket of his coveralls when he saw her. His face wreathed in smiles, he walked over to the car.

She was enveloped in a welcoming hug that nearly lifted her off the ground. For as tall as she was, he was taller, with a mane of gray-white hair that vividly contrasted with the sun-darkened color of his skin. His eyes were green like her own and his face was creased by many years of hard work.

"Welcome back, honey," he said, releasing her. And to Johnny, "Thank you for picking Kit up. Why don't you come in for a cool drink?"

"No thanks, Matt, I've got to get back. And anyway," he said, glancing at Kit, "the pleasure was mine."

They stood arm in arm as he reversed the car and turned it down the mountain. Then her uncle picked up her suitcase and they climbed the side stairs into the house. Despite the summer heat the inside of the house was cool and smelled as if it had been freshly waxed. The wooden banister gleamed with polish and the hardwood floors shone.

"Where's Willy?"

"Her granddaughter is moving into her own apartment so she went to help her get things organized. But she did leave some cookies and lemonade. Can I interest you in some?" he asked, grinning and knowing full well that there was nothing she liked better than Willy's chocolate chip cookies.

"You sure can and you know it. Let me get out of these clothes and I'll be right down."

As she unzipped her dress she realized that she would have to tell him straight out that she had been unsuccessful in finding any more buyers. He would be too perceptive to see through small talk or attempts to soften the truth of her failure. She finished undressing and then scooped up her clothes and set them on her bed. She would unpack later, for now she wanted a shower.

Later, sitting in the sunny kitchen, nibbling on chocolate chip cookies and drinking ice cold lemonade, she broke the bad news to her uncle. He took it calmly, almost as if he expected it.

"I'm sorry I couldn't get any commitments on this trip. Maybe I'll go again later in the summer."

"You did your best, Kit, but I think that even if you had gotten some buyers we would still be in trouble." As he spoke she thought how tired he looked. His eyes seemed to have lost their sparkle and his shoulders slumped forward. Still, he was a giant of a man and she knew he was not easily defeated. He had worked too long and hard on making the winery work to give up easily.

"What are we going to do?" she asked.

He pushed his fingers through his thick hair

and looked at her. "I've found someone who is interested in the winery."

"You mean you're going to sell it?" she asked in alarm.

"No, nothing like that. I'm thinking that I might sell a half interest in it and use the money to make repairs and buy the kinds of equipment I need to make more wine. That's why you didn't interest anyone in selling our product, honey. We just don't produce enough to make it worth their while."

She digested this bit of news for a moment. "Uncle Matt, I just can't see you having a partner. You've owned this winery and done things your own way for so long that I can't see you sharing the decisions with someone else."

"In a way I already have. Kit, honey, when you were having trouble with Tom and came back here to live, I was having financial troubles. I didn't want you to know because you needed me and this house and the winery and so I took out a personal loan to tide me over."

"But you could have told me," she said weakly, the enormity of what he was now telling her striking home. "I would have gotten a job, I would have . . ."

"Don't you see, you weren't in any shape to do that and then after Tom was killed you had your own problems to work out."

She was thoughtful for a moment. He was right. "Where did you get this loan?" she asked him.

"From an old friend, someone you've never met. And now he thinks he can help me out again."

"By buying half of the winery?"

"Kit, please listen for a moment. It's better to own half a winery than none at all. If we keep on the way things are going I won't own anything in a few years."

"I won't let you do it. I'll get a job in San Francisco with an advertising agency. I'll send you money every month."

"Honey, you may not have noticed but I'm getting on in years. I'm slowing down and maybe this offer has come at the right time. I could afford to hire a manager to help me. You have your own life to live, I don't want you to be tied to the winery."

"You don't understand. The winery is my life just as it is yours." Kit spoke those words and then suddenly felt very tired. Her futile trip to the east, her heart-wrenching experience with Adam Redmont and now the sad news about the winery made her feel drained.

Her uncle studied her face for a moment. "I wouldn't have told you this right after your trip except that the prospective buyer will be here tomorrow and I didn't want to spring this on you any later. That's why I couldn't pick you up. One of the hoses broke and I had to fix it. I want this place to be in top condition when he comes."

"I can't let you do this," she said weakly.

"Look, there is nothing final yet. Why don't

you wait until tomorrow and then I'll be able to tell you more."

She stood up and walked over to where he was sitting and kissed him on the forehead. "I love you," she whispered.

"I know that," he said, putting an arm around her waist and hugging her to him.

Later that evening as she prepared for bed she was still worried. It wasn't only the winery that troubled her, it was the house as well. She glanced around the old-fashioned bedroom, with its cheerful wallpaper of tiny flowers, her antique oak dresser and her brass bed and wondered if she would soon have to leave. Her room had the best view in the house. It looked out on a creek that ran down the mountainside and on a grove of redwood trees that stood silently guarding the mountain. What if the new partner wanted to live in part of the house? What if he wanted her bedroom and her uncle's bedroom for his wife and children?

She lay on her back, her hands behind her head, staring up at the ceiling. The decision was not yet final. Maybe she could still persuade her uncle to let her help in some way. He had carried the burden alone for too long. Even Willy confided that she was concerned about him.

After Willy had returned from her granddaughter's apartment, she and Kit had cooked dinner together. They talked about the winery and the decision her uncle was considering and Willy shook her head.

"I worry about him, Kit. He has lost some of his energy and seems terribly tired. But, you can't tell him anything of course. Least of all to slow down."

Kit couldn't remember when she had started calling Sara Williams, their small sprightly housekeeper, "Willy." She had given her the nickname when she was a small child and Willy had come to live with them and take care of her. Sara Williams was a widow with her own family to raise so she had worked days for Matt Carson. Later, when her children had grown she moved into the house and took her place as part of the family.

Kit smiled ruefully and wondered what Willy would say if she knew that her uncle had admitted to her that he was getting on in years. No, she would never know because he would keep up a front for Willy just as he had for her.

Maybe he sensed that she had put her experience with Tom behind her and was ready to face life again. He was right; she felt nothing for Tom anymore, but she felt a deep abiding love for her uncle.

She remembered the day she had come to live with him. He took her to his tiny house in St. Helena and told her she would stay with him forever and he would always be there to love her. And he has been, she reflected. Despite the fact that he had never approved of her marriage to Tom. "He'll break your heart," he had warned her when she told him they were going to get married. But, when he was proved right and she came back to live with him, he took her in and never said I-told-you-so.

For the first time since the drive home from the airport, the handsome face of Adam Redmont flitted into her mind. She wondered what her uncle would have said about him. Would he have advised her that he would break her heart? Well, she would never know because she would never see him again.

She was up early the next morning and dressed casually in white slacks and a dark green T-shirt tank top. As she came downstairs to breakfast she saw her uncle seated at the kitchen table and Willy serving him waffles. She kissed them both.

"You had a call from a young man a few minutes ago," he grinned.

She took a sip of juice. "Anyone I know?" she teased.

"Johnny said he'd be here in a half hour to take you to Angie's. She has some news to tell you."

She laughed. "I can't resist an order, even if it comes from Johnny."

"He cares for you, Kit. A good deal, I think," Willy added.

"I know. I care for him, too, like a brother. Ye gods, we've known each other for ages." And then, deliberately changing the subject, she turned to her uncle. "When is your business appointment?"

"Later this afternoon."

She nodded and sat down while Willy loaded her plate with waffles.

"Hey, not so much," she laughingly protested.

"You need to put some meat on your bones. Didn't you eat at all while you were in New York?" Willy grumbled.

"No one cooks like you, Willy, so of course I was totally dissatisfied with any of the food," she grinned impishly.

"You're right, no one does," her uncle said quietly.

It was not until she sat in Angie's living room listening to her talk about her expected baby that she wondered about her uncle and the housekeeper. Willy had been looking after her uncle for years. Could they be in love with each other? She had been so wrapped up in her own problems for the last few years that she hadn't paid much attention to the two people she cared most about in the world.

"Kit, you're not listening," dark-haired Angie pouted prettily.

"That's all she's done since I brought her. You haven't let her get a word in edgewise," Johnny joked back.

Kit snapped out of her daydreaming and brought her attention back to Angie. "I'm sorry, what did you say?"

"I said that the folks have planned a big barbecue next weekend to tell the whole valley about their expected grandchild and you're invited, of course."

"Oh, Angie, you know I wouldn't miss it. I'm so happy for you," she replied. And then, glancing at Johnny, who was lounging on an easy chair, she began softly. "My mind has been wandering I'll admit. I'm worried about Uncle Matt."

Briefly she told them about the state of finances of the winery and about her uncle's proposal.

"Oh, no, Kit," Angie said. "Perhaps I could ask Papa to help."

"No," she interrupted gently, "I'm just worried about him, that's all. Uncle Matt is such a stubborn, independent old cuss, he would never accept help from your family, or anyone, not even me."

Angie nodded her understanding and reached over and squeezed Kit's hand. "I know it will work out," she said.

Johnny was silent for the first part of the drive home. Finally he said quietly, "I may have a solution to your problem, Kit."

"Hmmm, what's that?"

"Marry me," he said softly.

She turned to look at him. There was a solemn earnestness to his face and she knew this moment had been coming for a long time. There was no easy way to say it without hurting him.

"I can't do that, Johnny," she said gently.

"Why?"

"Because I love you like a brother, not like a woman should love the man she marries."

"You mean not like you loved Tom," he said bitterly.

"That was long ago and I was very young. But I've learned a lot since then and one thing I know now is that you deserve more than I feel for you."

"Ouch," he yelped in mock pain. "I know," he admitted, "I guess I've always known. Still, I want to help you, Kit. Let me."

"I don't know what you or anyone else can do right now. Uncle Matt is determined to keep everything strictly business. But I appreciate the offer."

"You'll let me take you to the barbecue?"

"Of course."

As they drew up to the house she saw a small green foreign sports car parked in the driveway. She guessed that it would belong to the businessman who was talking to her uncle, and thought it funny that he would have a sports car. She had pictured a very large, silver sedan. After all, he would be very staid and very practical.

She said goodbye to Johnny and stood on the outside stairs a moment before going into the house. Naturally her uncle would introduce her to his guest and she would try to be pleasant. She would try to understand that to this businessman the winery meant dollars and cents. There was no room for sentiment or feelings as far as he would be concerned. He would look at the books and decide if the investment would be a good one. The people involved would not matter.

This meeting would be difficult for her, but then she supposed it was difficult for her proud stubborn uncle, too. Opening the front door, she heard voices coming from the living room. The oak sliding doors were shut but she could still hear voices and what she thought was the sound of laughter. She'd better get it over with. Straightening her T-shirt tank top and wishing for a moment that she had put on a more respectable outfit, she knocked on the door.

"Come in," her uncle called.

She pushed aside the doors with both hands and entered the room. Then she stopped dead still at what she saw. There, sitting on the old-fashioned divan, his long legs crossed in front of him, his gray eyes riveted to her, was Adam Redmont.

"You!" she choked out.

"Hello, Kitten," he said.

Chapter Four

She stood unable to move or utter another sound.

"I was going to introduce you to my niece Kit, Adam, but it appears as if you two have already met."

Adam stood up and looked at her with an amused expression on his lips and a gleam in his silvery eyes. "Yes, we have," he said reaching out his hand to her.

Suddenly the realization of what had happened on the airplane struck her. He had used her. She pulled her hand away as if it were resting on a hot stove. Seeing her action her uncle's eyebrows shot up. She said simply, "We met on the airplane yesterday."

Adam's lips twitched silently before he replied, "Yes, Matt, I met your niece on the airplane and we had quite an interesting conversation."

"Well, that's fine," her uncle said, not missing the undercurrents that were swirling around the room. "Why don't we all sit down."

Kit felt an anger welling up in her so strong that she wanted to reach out and strike that handsome face. But instead she turned and found the nearest chair across the room from him. He had pumped her for information about the winery, knowing full well who she was and where she came from, and the crazy thing was that she had believed that he was interested in her.

"I was just telling Adam that there is no need for him to find a motel. We have a large house and he is welcome to stay here while he looks over the winery's operation."

Her uncle looked at her for affirmation and she was tempted to tell him that Adam Redmont was certainly not welcome in this house but she caught his silent appeal for her to agree and so she forced a smile on her lips and said stiffly, "Of course he can stay here."

She knew she sounded insincere and Adam knew it, too, for he looked at her, a broad grin appearing on his handsome face, and said, "I can't refuse such a kind offer. I accept your hospitality."

Later, as she showered and dressed for dinner she marveled over the fact that she had been able to carry on any kind of civil conversation at all. The seething anger she felt at being used made her confine her answers to the questions he asked her about the business to yes and no, and finally, giving up, he turned to her uncle for more information.

He knew she was angry. Yes, handsome Adam Redmont knew that she was so angry that she wanted to strike him and he was amused by it. More than once during the conversation she saw him looking at her with the beginnings of a smile on his face. She had amused him. He had played with her on the airplane as a cat plays with a mouse and when she had succumbed to his charm and told him everything he wanted to know he had walked away seeking other conquests.

She sat down on her bed and brushed her hair in swift angry strokes. Now he was going to stay in her house and inspect the winery and she was powerless to do anything about it. Or was she?

As she dressed an idea formed in her mind. Why not fight fire with fire? Why not turn on the charm as he had done with her and find out all she could about him. There must be some weakness, some chink in his armor, and when she found it she could use it against him in the same way he was using the information she had given him.

Her dress was a violet-colored cotton with a deeply scooped neck and a softly gathered skirt. Tiny straps over her shoulders left a great deal of her neck and creamy shoulders exposed and she started to put on a necklace of purple stones but then changed her mind. She left her hair loose on her shoulders and surveyed herself in the mirror. The dress revealed a great deal of her feminine charms as it clung to her full breasts and slim waist. She smiled a delighted smile. We'll see who uses who, Mr. Redmont, she said to herself.

They ate dinner in the old-fashioned dining room, which was dominated by a large oval oak table. Willy brought out her delicious stewed chicken dish and Adam commented on how her cooking would rival the greatest restaurants. Kit was disgusted by the flattery and his obvious attempts to win Willy to his side.

She glanced over at him and saw that he was looking at her. His blue shirt and gray sport slacks made him look more attractive than she remembered. She decided that if she was going to put her plan to work she might as well get started.

Smiling sweetly, she began with, "Isn't Willy a fabulous cook, Adam?"

His eyes followed the soft swell of her breasts before meeting her gaze. "Yes, she is, I've never tasted a more delicious chicken."

"Do you do your own cooking?" she asked.

"Only when I have to, Kit. Mostly when I'm traveling I eat out."

"And you travel a great deal?"

"As much as I have to," was his noncommittal reply.

"Your company sends you all over the country, I suppose?"

"Kit, let the man eat his dinner," her uncle interjected.

"Of course," she said giving Adam her most gracious smile and noticing his look of enjoyment at the entertainment she was providing.

After dinner she usually helped Willy with the dishes, but tonight she was ordered out of the kitchen to keep their guest company and she joined Adam and her uncle on the veranda. The night was warm as they sat sipping her uncle's favorite port and watching the stars glow in the darkened sky.

"Have you seen much of the wine country, Adam?"

"Not too much, Matt. The time that I have for myself I use for soaring. I guess I've seen more from the air than I have from the ground."

"You ought to have Kit show you around while you're here. She knows this valley better than most people."

"I would like that and in exchange I'll take her soaring."

"What do you say, Kit?" her uncle asked.

"Of course. That sounds like a fair exchange," she said trying to sound enthusiastic. "If you want to see the large wineries you can just walk in and go on a tour. They have them every day. The smaller operations, like ours, schedule them by appointment because everyone is too busy making wine to stop and give tours. Everyone has tasting rooms. Ours is in the retail shop at the bottom of the hill."

"Very interesting," he said.

Because they sat in darkness she could not see his face; she could only hear the amusement in his voice.

"Well, I'm going to turn in for the evening. You two have a good chat," her Uncle Matt said, and Kit could swear he too sounded amused.

After he left, she stood up. If everything she said was so funny, she might as well give up for the evening and go to bed herself.

"I guess I'll go to bed, too. Good night, Adam," she said.

He stood up and put his hands on her shoulders. "Just a minute, I think we have something to talk about."

"Do you?" she asked. Those strong hands, those treacherous hands, resting on her bare shoulders were beginning to have an effect on her.

"Yes I do. Why were you so angry this afternoon?"

"I was . . . surprised to see you."

"No, you were more than surprised, Kitten. You looked like you would like to get your claws into me and scratch my eyes out."

Now the hands were drifting from her shoulders to her back and were holding her inches away from his tall powerful masculine frame. In the darkness she could not see the gray eyes but she knew they were staring at her and for one moment her resolve weakened.

"You might have mentioned that you knew about the winery. I asked you, remember?"

"Yes, you did ask me and I might have mentioned it but I didn't want to."

"Oh, I see."

"You see nothing. I wanted to find out about you, not about the winery."

"I don't believe you."

"Then believe this."

His lips came down on hers gently, caressing her own, and her heart thudded in her chest with wild pleasure. She parted her lips and responded because deep down this was what she had wanted, too. He molded her to the length of him, kissing her as if he could not get enough of her.

"You're so soft, my green-eyed Kitten," he murmured in a hoarse voice as he stroked her bare shoulders.

Her arms crept up around his neck and she strained toward him pressing her breasts into his broad chest. Her senses reeled at the devastating feel of him against her as he rained kisses over her face and her neck. His hand gently brushed aside one of the tiny shoulder straps and his lips plundered the pulsing cord of her neck and the shadowy valley between her breasts.

The feel of him touching her with his lips and his gentle hands had a telling effect on her. *Don't stop, don't stop,* she begged with her body.

"This is what I've wanted to do from the moment we met," he whispered.

For Kit it was as if a splash of cold water were suddenly thrown in her face. The deception on the airplane, the plan to buy the winery, that was what Adam Redmont wanted. She suddenly pulled back from his arms.

"You've no need to tell me what you wanted from the moment we met," she said icily, "You wanted the winery."

"You couldn't possibly know what I want, Kitten," he answered in an oddly husky voice.

So he thought her a fool as well. "You want this winery and you must think I'm naive not to know it. You got me to tell you all about it on the airplane to make it easier for yourself. Is that how your investment firm works? They send you out to charm the clients?" she shot back angrily, adjusting her shoulder strap into place.

"You're wrong, Kitten, very wrong," his voice was ominously low. "If you'd waited at the airport . . ."

But he got no further because the picture of the woman in the maroon suit in his arms was too much to bear. "You are despicable," she shouted. "If I can help it you will not get one piece of this winery."

She turned and, before he could stop her,

ran into the house and up to her bedroom. As she stood behind the closed door, taking deep heaving breaths, she knew that her plans to charm him would never work. He had only to touch her and she forgot everything but the feel of him. She would never get more information about him by being cooperative; the only alternative left was to be as uncooperative as possible and see if she could thwart him in his designs on the winery.

For the next two days she successfully avoided Adam. She ate her meals alone while he and her uncle were going over the winery records. While they were out looking at the vineyards from which Silverado purchased grapes, she worked in the retail store.

It was a small structure at the bottom of the hill across the highway from the winery. It consisted of a storeroom and a larger room built of redwood and lined with display racks filled with bottles of Silverado wine. Kit and a young college student, Lisa Gerard, sold wine and poured small quantities into glasses for customer tastings.

Lisa was younger than Kit and came from a large family. She worked at a variety of jobs while she was going to school at night. She hid her shyness behind large round glasses and a hairdo that pulled her long dark hair into an unbecoming bun at the base of her neck.

Every summer for the past couple of years Lisa had worked full time at the retail shop with Kit. They had become friends, despite the other girl's shyness and got along well together. This summer the tourist traffic passing through the valley was brisk, and they were kept busy ringing up sales and telling people about Silverado wine while they poured sample tastes. It was work they both enjoyed, especially Kit, who often got involved in answering questions and telling people about the other wineries in the valley and the places that would make good picnic stops.

At the end of a particularly busy day Kit looked up from the cash register as the bell suspended above the door announced that someone had entered the shop. She smiled as she saw Johnny's familiar face. Lisa looked up from her job of restocking the shelves and then retreated into the storeroom.

"Hello, can I interest you in some competitor's wine?" Kit asked mischievously.

"My family would never forgive me," he joked back, "but actually I stopped by to check on tomorrow night. The barbecue will start at seven and I thought I'd pick you up at a quarter to."

"Fine." She rearranged some small gift boxes as she talked. The busy day had taken its toll on the orderliness of the shop.

She was reaching up to stack one more box on a pile of empties to complete a display on the counter when she felt Johnny's hand touching the small of her back.

"Let me help you with that, Kit," he offered, and she turned to face him.

The bell tinkled at that moment as the door of the shop swung open. Kit was standing so close to Johnny that she had a hard time seeing the customer. Lisa came from the storeroom at that moment and her soft "Oh" filled the quiet shop. Quickly Kit stepped from behind Johnny and her eyes met the cool glare of Adam Redmont.

"I hope I'm not interrupting anything," he said.

"Did you wish to purchase some wine?" she asked him in a voice so brisk that both Lisa and Johnny looked at her in surprise.

"Matt told me you would show me the facilities," he replied, ignoring her rudeness.

Trapped, she introduced him to Lisa and Johnny and explained that he was staying at their house for a few days while he and her uncle discussed business arrangements.

Johnny shook his hand in a friendly manner and Lisa said softly, "I'm happy to meet you."

Kit could not believe her ears when she heard Johnny invite him to come to the Angelli barbecue. He accepted and then quickly asked Lisa if she would come as his date.

"Of course, I should have thought of that myself. Angie would love to see you again, Lisa," Johnny said, looking over at the shy girl with the large round glasses.

I might have known he would not be coming alone, Kit thought. Mr. Handsome always

72

had to have an adoring female in tow somewhere. Not that she was jealous. Quiet, shy
Lisa Gerard would not be a match for the
attractive man now standing before her, she
thought in disgust.

"Kit, I have to take care of the twins this
afternoon. Mind if I leave a little early?" Lisa
asked, her cheeks tinged with pink.

"Go ahead, I'll lock up," Kit replied.

"Let me run you home," Johnny offered and
Lisa gratefully nodded and went to the back to
fetch her purse.

"The party starts at seven, Adam. Kit can
give you directions. Be sure to make the proper noises over Angie, my parents are nuts
about grandchildren," Johnny said.

"So are mine," Adam responded quietly,
looking over at Kit.

Lisa returned, carrying her purse, and the
two of them departed. Kit stood silently
watching Adam glance around the shop. His
eyes traveled over the display of wine, the gift
packs and the counter with the tasting glasses
set up in one corner. Then they rested on Kit.

"Your boyfriend?"

"None of your business."

"My, we are snapping today, Kitten. Sheath
your claws and show me the back room."

She turned and walked into the storeroom
area. He followed her and she became anxious about the fact that the two of them were
now alone together. She would try to get this
over with as soon as possible.

"We sell wine by the bottle out there and also by the case. We also ship gift packages for people and sell to small restaurants."

"Yes, your literature explains that," he said, holding a small pamphlet that Kit had designed. They had been stacked in one corner of the counter and he must have picked one up as he walked by.

"Well, that's all there is to see," she said stiffly.

He took a step closer. "Is it?" he asked.

She noticed that the blue denim shirt he wore was unbuttoned at the neck. Dark hairs peeked out where the upper part of his chest was exposed. The sight of him standing so close, looking at her with his gray eyes, unnerved her. She had to get him out of there.

"It is. Now if you'll excuse me. . . . I need to lock up."

He moved closer still, his broad shoulders blocking out her view of the rest of the room.

"You can look around if you like," she said, gesturing with her hand.

He caught it and held it securely in his own.

"Let me go."

"No, not until you listen to what I have to say."

"I don't want to hear it."

"You will hear it, by God," he muttered pulling her closer still until their bodies were almost touching. Then he released her hand and held her shoulders firmly in his grasp.

She tried to fight the feelings of arousal as

his thumbs absently rubbed her shoulders and the way her heart was thudding in her chest as the smoky eyes met hers.

"I did not use the meeting on the airplane to find out about the winery. I wanted to find out about you. When I realized who you were it was too late to tell you about my reasons for coming to the Bay Area."

"I don't believe you."

He went on as if she hadn't spoken. "Your uncle mentioned that he had a niece but I had no idea . . ."

"No idea of what?" she interrupted. Anything to force him to stop looking at her as if he were going to make love to her.

"That you were a green-eyed kitten who could be soft and gentle one minute and clawing and spitting the next."

"Let go of me," she repeated.

"Make me," he said in a silky voice.

It was hard to pull away when she wanted to melt into his arms and feel his lips on her own. Damn! She would not be used by another attractive man. She tried to wrench herself free.

"No way," he whispered, pulling her into his arms.

The lips that touched hers were gentle and teasing, as they had been that night on the veranda. As much as she tried to stand passively under their attempt to arouse her, she felt a growing ache to respond.

Then, slowly, the teasing changed into a

sensual assault. His tongue probed her tightly closed lips, his hand massaged the back of her neck while the other caught a handful of her hair and let it spill between his fingers.

She weakened for a moment and parted her lips for him. That was all he needed. His tongue flicked over her lips and made forays into her mouth. A rising excitement was sweeping her body as he continued his assault.

Before she knew it she was responding, kissing him back with abandon, feeling the muscular length of him against her and hearing the excited beating of her own heart.

"Kitten, you drive me out of my mind, you know that," he said in a raw husky voice.

He rained kisses on her face and with one hand, unbuttoned one of the buttons of her blouse to reach the softness of her neck while his other hand cupped her breast.

She gasped in delight at the exquisite feelings that raced through her body. He had only to touch her and she fell apart. It was as if a dam had burst within her and the feelings that she had kept bottled up for so long surged through in one wild moment.

They clung to each other in the storeroom of the retail shop, kissing and touching and wanting each other, oblivious to anything else.

The bell sounded in the other room, telling them that someone had entered the shop. Kit came to her senses first and pulled back from his embrace.

"Kit! Adam!" It was her Uncle Matt.

"We're back in the storeroom," Adam said raising his voice to be heard.

As the footsteps make their way to the back room she quickly buttoned the top button of her blouse and smoothed down her hair.

"Trust me, that's all I ask," he said in a low voice before her uncle came through the doorway.

She wanted to, she told him with her eyes, but she had lost the ability to trust.

Chapter Five

$\mathcal{T}$ he next night, as she stood in front of the mirror, critically surveying her halter-top dress in the same color of jade green as her eyes, she remembered Adam's words, "Trust me." If only she could.

Last night she had eaten dinner with him and her uncle and finally learned something about him. His father, it turned out, was the old friend her uncle had mentioned. The two men had met years ago when she was a youngster and Adam's father had lent her uncle money on more than one occasion.

The family lived in Virginia but Adam had an older brother who lived somewhere in northern California with his wife and three children. All of the family members had at one time or another worked in the investment firm begun by his grandfather. Adam's interest in winemaking was the reason he had been sent to the Napa Valley to represent his father and the firm.

She admitted to herself that there did not seem to be anything devious or secretive about him. Still, she could not bring herself to believe that he wasn't using the fact that she found him attractive to get her to go along with his plan to purchase a half-interest in the winery.

Trying to hurry before Johnny arrived, she searched the room for her strappy white sandals. Perhaps her uncle might be able to get a loan from somewhere else to help him out of his current difficulties and still keep total control of the winery.

Thinking about her uncle brought another worried frown to her face. He had looked so tired and drawn these past few days that she was very concerned about him. She had questioned him about his health several times since her arrival home, but he always brushed off her concerns with a smile and an admonition not to worry.

She heard a knock at the bedroom door just as she managed to find one of her shoes and slip it on. Still holding the other one in her hand she limped over to the door and opened it.

Adam stood in the doorway, wearing charcoal gray slacks and a white shirt that made his hair look blacker than ever and made him look even more virile and masculine than he had before.

"Yes?"

He surveyed her from head to toe, his eyes resting on the halter top which exposed a great deal of her shoulders and neck before it clung to her thrusting breasts. As he noticed that she was holding one of her shoes, a smile played on his lips.

"I came to get directions to Lisa's house and to the Angelli barbecue, but I see you need some help, Kitten," he said, moving past her into the bedroom.

"What do you mean I need some help?"

He put his hands around her waist and gently eased her over to the bed.

"What do you think you're doing?"

"Easy now," he murmured as he took her shoe from her hand and lifted her bare foot into his hands.

Before slipping the shoe on her foot he gently caressed her ankles and the tender skin on top of her foot, causing a tingling sensation to race up her leg. His touch made her all the more aware of the devastating effect he could have on her if she let him. Then, slowly, he slid the shoe on and pushed the strap into place behind her heel.

"Okay, Kitten," he said softly, taking her hand and pulling her upright.

As she stood up she was very aware of the fact that he was looking at her with silvery eyes that stripped the halter top from her body and exposed her firm high breasts beneath. This brought her back to reality.

"What do you mean coming in here like this? Who do you think you are?"

"Calm down, Kitten," he replied. "You let me in, remember? I came to get directions."

She had forgotten the barbecue in the brief few minutes with him. Silently she cursed herself for her weakness.

"Move aside and I'll give them to you."

To her surprise he did so without argument and she reached her bureau without his touching her further. She fumbled with the drawer in her nervousness to get him out of her bedroom and finally extracted a pad of paper and a pencil. Quickly she wrote the directions to Lisa's house on one side of the top sheet and the directions to the Angelli residence on the other. Then she turned and hurriedly thrust the paper at him.

"Here."

Ignoring her outstretched hand, he asked, "Why are you so eager to get rid of me, I wonder?"

"Look, you wanted directions, well here they are."

Very slowly he reached out, took the paper from her and put it into his pants pocket.

"Is Johnny your boyfriend?" he asked suddenly.

Surprised by this she was caught off guard.

"I've known him for ages, I grew up with the Angellis. I . . . used to be married to his older brother."

"Used to be?"

"Yes, used to be, now please go."

He was quiet for a moment and she saw the gray eyes glance down to her hand and quickly scan her fingers for a ring. Then without another word he turned and left the room.

Why, she asked herself, did he have such an unnerving effect on her merely by being in the same room with her? And why did she allow his touch to make her so nervous? Surely she was past all of that. She was no longer the adoring young girl who had married her handsome neighbor. She was a realist, Tom had seen to that. No man could be trusted. Adam Redmont was to be trusted less than others. He was rich, he was handsome and he wanted something from her uncle. He had asked her to trust him, but how could she? Besides, he hadn't yet explained about the maroon sophisticate who had met him at the airport. Maybe he never intended to.

This time the knock at the door interrupting her thoughts was Willy telling her that Johnny was downstairs. She gathered her lacy knit shawl over her shoulders and went down to meet him.

They said good night to her uncle, who was busy in his study pouring over documents, and as they reached the doorway Johnny whispered, "You look beautiful tonight, Kit."

"Thanks," she replied, her mind still trying to shut out the way those gray eyes had boldly undressed her a few moments before.

As they drove to Johnny's house Kit puzzled over the way her life had suddenly become very complicated. Adam Redmont had only to touch her and she wanted him never to stop. Yet she could not trust herself with him, nor could she trust him with her.

"You're being awfully quiet tonight, Kit. Is Matt all right?"

"I'm sorry, Johnny. Yes, of course, that is, I think so," she mumbled.

He looked over at her briefly but did not respond.

The Angelli winery was set back several miles from the road. A heavy wooden sign hung from the arched entrance to the drive. As they passed through it they were surrounded on both sides of the road by delicate locust trees that lined the drive and made a fragile barrier between it and the Angelli vineyards.

To her right a series of large stone buildings held the crushers and the stainless steel tanks of the Angelli winery. But Johnny took a left turn away from the winery and followed the road up the side of a steeply rising plateau. There, gleaming in the setting sun, was the Angelli residence. A giant three-tiered structure that overlooked the vineyards, it had been built by his grandfather at the end of the last century to resemble an Italian villa. The stones that formed its base were dazzling white, and as the car turned into the inner courtyard, a profusion of brightly colored flowers lining the entrance to the house came into view.

"I've always thought that your home is one of the most beautiful in the valley," she said.

"It could be yours, too, Kit," he replied.

"Johnny . . . I . . ."

"I know, Kit, sorry," he was smiling ruefully. "It's a hard dream to give up." He reached over and squeezed her hand. "Promise I won't bring it up again. Let's go in."

The lawn behind the house was full of people laughing and talking when they entered. Kit knew most of them because they were all people from the valley. Angie was the center of attention, naturally, and her big husky husband Ray stood nearby while she greeted the guests.

Despite the fact that Angie was and probably always would be a scene stealer and an outrageous flirt, Kit knew that she was deeply in love with Ray and delighted about her pregnancy.

"Kit, Kit," she squealed as Johnny led her through the crowd to his sister. She threw her arms around Kit's shoulders and gave her a hug, and then, because she was the same changeable Angie that Kit had grown to love over the years, whispered, "Is everything all right at home?"

Kit smiled, and nodded; this was not the

time and place to tell her about the private agony that she was experiencing. Angie would find out soon enough anyway, she was too perceptive not to.

As if reading her mind, Angie turned to the couple who had just arrived. "You must be Adam Redmont. And, Lisa, it's good to see you again."

Kit stepped aside so that they could be introduced to Angie's husband and as she did so she noticed that Lisa's face glowed with a warmth she had never seen before. Her soft hair was brushed smoothly over her shoulders and her dress, a delicate shade of coral, accentuated her slim figure.

A sharp pain of jealousy shot through her as she saw Adam's arm draped around Angie's shoulders. So that was the reason for the smile, he had cast his spell on her as well. She could not bear to look at them together. She turned and made her way over to greet Mama and Papa Angelli.

The sun set in a blazing ball of fire and the barbecue fires were lit. Paper lanterns were hung from trees in the spacious backyard and as dusk turned to darkness their glowing lights gave a festive air to the party.

More guests arrived. The entire valley must have been invited to celebrate the upcoming birth of this first Angelli grandchild. Dinner was served, buffet style, and Adam became lost in the crowd. Actually Kit had to admit to herself that she was avoiding him by burying herself among old friends and shifting the talk to early school days and laughing reminiscences.

After dinner the outside speakers attached to the house carried the sounds of the latest music and couples drifted into each other's arms to dance or formed small groups to sit in the lawn chairs to laugh and talk. One subject was never mentioned, Tom. It was as if he had never existed. The Angelli's were proud people and the behavior of their son had hurt them deeply. Now all of the attention was focused on the arrival of their first grandchild and their second son, who would inherit the business.

Kit danced with Johnny several times and with some of her other friends, but finally drifted off to stand beside a low retaining wall in a darkened corner of the yard.

The stars twinkled in the dark sky and she felt for a moment as if she were totally alone in the universe with their glowing presence. A sound to her left caused her to turn her back to the wall.

"Stargazing?" The voice was unmistakable.

"Do you mind? I came here to be alone for a few minutes."

"You don't really want to be alone, do you, Kitten?" He came closer.

"Yes, as a matter of fact, I do."

"Where is your sense of romance? The beautiful summer night, the beautiful woman and the . . ."

"Handsome man," she finished for him. "No thanks, I've been there before."

"So that's what it is, he must have hurt you badly."

"That is none of your business."

She turned her back to him, gazing out at the darkened vineyards, dismissing him. But he would not be dismissed. She felt his hands on her shoulders and she was pulled back against his hard chest.

"I intend to make it my business. Tell me, Kitten, what did he do to make you so bitter?"

For some reason the feeling of being securely held in those strong arms and leaning against his broad chest in the darkened garden gave her a sense of security that she had not known for a long time. If only she could lean on him. She wanted to trust him, but. . . .

"Tell me," he whispered in her ear.

It was easier to tell him if she didn't have to look into his eyes. Besides, he would find out soon enough anyway. Everyone in the valley knew what had happened.

"I married Tom Angelli right out of college and the marriage didn't work out. That's all there is to tell."

But he would have none of it. "Why didn't it work out?" he asked gently.

She stirred in his arms. "He ran around with other women. He gambled. He . . . he didn't want the kind of life I did. I left him and moved back in with my uncle. He died in an automobile crash with his girlfriend."

She felt him stiffen as she said the last part and heard the slow release of breath. Then, gently, he turned her around in his arms until she faced him. The moonlight gleamed on his mouth and his gray eyes. But the expression on his face was not one of pity, it was one of anger.

"It's a good thing he's dead because I could kill him for what he did to you," he said in a low voice.

"Oh, I'm a big girl now. I've put away my childish dreams," she said, attempting to sound lighthearted about the whole incident.

"Don't give me that. You don't believe it and neither do I. You're bitter and mistrustful because you were hurt badly. I don't know what your dreams were, Kitten, but you shouldn't bury them away. No one should."

This was the first time he had spoken so seriously since they had met. There was none of the teasing amusement that she had come to recognize in his voice. It was as if her words had moved him. She was intrigued and frightened at the same time. She could deal with the teasing easily but this new Adam Redmont was definitely more dangerous.

"And what are your dreams?" she asked, "Have you hung onto them?"

"Yes, I have," he replied. "I've always

thought that owning a winery and living in the country would be the best kind of life for me. This is a beautiful valley and I've been coming here every time I've had a chance to travel to the Bay Area. Each time I've grown more and more fond of it."

She turned back to the darkness and he pulled her gently against him. His lips were in her hair and the heady nearness of him was having a riotous effect on her determination to resist him. For some strange reason she couldn't summon the anger necessary to pull away. Desperately she sought to keep the conversation going.

"I've always thought that big businesses that become partners with smaller ones were really only interested in forcing them out. In my mind they are big impersonal things incapable of feelings and human compassion. Profits are the only thing they understand. . . . But yours is a family-owned business. . . ."

"You're very adept at changing the subject. Yes, it's a family-owned business begun by my grandfather and now run by his sons and grandsons."

"Tell me about it."

"Now? Here with the moonlight and the stars? I hardly think this is the place or time to talk business."

His lips wandered down the side of her neck and made light forays across her shoulders. She breathed a shaky breath, trying to still the delicious feeling that was stealing across her body. Then he was lifting her hair from her shoulders and kissing her nape with feather light kisses that brought a gasp from her lips.

A sound of laughter nearby startled her. He felt her stiffen, released her from his arms and turned her to face him.

"I want to get to know you better, Kitten, and I want you to get to know me. But if we stay here any longer I'll untie the knot at the back of your neck that holds up this tantalizing dress and carry you off to the bushes."

She felt a delicious warmth where he had kissed her and for one crazy moment she thought of untying the knot herself and feeling those warm hands on her body. A shiver passed through her at her erotic thoughts.

"You're cold, let's go back. But first . . . I'd like to take you soaring with me tomorrow. Will you come?"

"I . . ."

"We made a bargain. You show me the local wineries and I take you soaring. Are you going to go back on that?"

"Well no, but I haven't taken you anywhere."

"You will and tomorrow we go soaring."

Unable to summon anymore arguments she nodded in agreement.

"Good, come on you're shivering and I'm . . . forget it. Let's go back to the party."

Why she had agreed to come soaring with

him she didn't know. She supposed it was the moonlight and the magnetic attraction he had for her. Now, in the cool light of day, she had misgivings.

They had had to wait several days to go soaring because she had some afternoon tours booked and afternoons were the best times to go up. He had used the quiet morning hours of those days to lure her away from the retail shop and persuade her to take him to the smaller valley wineries. As she introduced him to the owners and listened to him ask questions about their operations she realized that behind his handsome face and easy grin was a keen business mind. She shouldn't have been surprised, but the seriousness with which he studied the wineries was in vivid contrast to the image she had of him as a rich, money-hungry businessman and she found herself slowly warming to the new Adam she saw and letting down her guard.

Today was one of those rare summer days when the breezes blowing in from San Francisco Bay penetrated the valley and brought a measure of coolness from the 90 degree temperatures of the previous days.

They had driven to Calistoga, a nearby town famous for its mineral spas and mud baths, in the early afternoon. The soaring center was located at the end of the main street and consisted of a grassy field intersected by a short runway and an open pavilion where arrangements could be made to take lessons or rent a sailplane.

Adam left her for a moment to check on his reservation and she stood on the grass watching the sailplanes move into place for their tows. They looked like fragile gulls with their short bodies and graceful wingspans. She had referred to them as gliders during the drive up but Adam had told her that a glider is any plane without an engine while a sailplane is a glider that can rise on upcurrents of air called thermals.

"Ready?" he asked, coming up to stand beside her.

"Yes," she said swallowing a lump in her throat. This was going to be worse than flying in a big jet.

"Relax, Kitten, you will be perfectly safe. We're going to be towed into the air by that small propeller-driven airplane and when we're over the ridge I'll pull the cable release knob and we'll float on the air currents."

She gulped. "Will we have parachutes?"

He turned to look at her. Cupping her chin in his hand, he said gently, "We won't need them. The weather is perfect and nothing is going to happen." Then he planted a quick kiss on the tip of her nose. "I wouldn't let anything happen to you, Kitten, don't you know that?"

"Mr. Redmont, your plane is ready," one of the assistants called out.

"Okay, be right there," he answered.

"You can't back out now," he said, his hands on her shoulders. "I'm not going to," she replied firmly. People do this all the time, she thought. Anyway, what has happened to the impulsive Kit Carson of long ago? "Let's go," she said with all of the enthusiasm she could put into her voice.

He led her to an orange-and-yellow-striped sailplane and lifted her into the cockpit. Carefully he strapped her in, then climbed into the seat in front of her and lowered himself.

The assistant helped lower the Plexiglas canopy into place, sealing the cockpit closed. Then he stepped to the front to attach the towrope. Kit watched as he held one of the wings of the sailplane to steady it for take-off.

Adam signalled to the other pilot that he was ready by wagging the plane's rudder with his control stick, and quickly the tow plane began pulling them down the runway.

In spite of her earlier resolve Kit tensed her body for the take-off and curled her fingers into tight fists. But the sailplane did not thrust itself noisily into the air the way large jets did. Instead, it lifted off the ground quietly and gracefully on the power provided by the tow plane. Instead of a great roar of jet engines, all she heard was a muted rush of air from the open side vents as the sailplane was towed to the ridge.

When they reached the hills which lined the

valley Adam pulled the cable release knob and there was a thud as the towrope was disengaged from the sailplane. The tow plane turned to return to the soaring center, the rope floating behind it in the wind.

"Look down there," he yelled over the whooshing air, pointing out the window.

Her first view of the Napa Valley from the air took her breath away. The verdant swath nestled between the hills looked like a patch of green velvet.

As they made a sweeping turn she tried to pick out familiar landmarks from the air. In the distance she caught a glimpse of Lake Hennessey and the small community of Pope Valley. Now, as they turned, she saw Mount St. Helena, after which the town was named.

Eagerly she began to scan the valley looking for wineries and vineyards. She saw the Angelli vineyards and the large white villa above them, gleaming in the sun.

Then, after another sweeping turn she tapped Adam on the shoulders excitedly. "Over there, over there, it's Silverado."

He twisted his head around to follow her pointing finger. Then he looked at her excited face and a brilliant smile lit up his own. "See what else you recognize, Kitten," he said.

The sailplane turned again, each time drifting lower over the valley. She continued to recognize the wineries that she and Adam had just visited, and it was not until she saw the soaring center that she realized that the fear had completely left her and all she had been feeling during the flight was excitement.

Their landing was bumpy as the sailplane's one wheel touched down and came to rest in a grassy area off the runway. She sat back in amazement. She had actually enjoyed the flight. Adam unstrapped himself and turned to face her.

"Is that all there is?" she grinned.

"You want more?" he asked. "The flight was short because I didn't know whether or not you'd like it. I just let gravity pull us down but if you want to go up again, this time I'll look for thermals and we'll stay up a little longer."

"Yes, yes, I want to. I can see why you like it. What a marvelous feeling that is, flying like the birds."

He leaned down and planted a gentle kiss on her lips. "I'm very glad you liked it, honey. If you're sure you want to go up again I'll go and arrange for another tow."

She nodded happily and he pushed back the canopy and climbed out of the sailplane. She turned to watch his long lean body move toward the pavilion. He was dressed casually in blue jeans and she noticed that there was a gracefulness to the way he moved that made her wonder if he had ever been an athlete. I know so little about him, she mused.

As he walked with his back toward her she saw an assistant run over to him and gesture in Kit's direction. Adam turned back for a quick glance at her and then took off running.

Something made her pause, as if to breathe deeply for a respite from something she knew was coming, and then quickly unfasten her seat belt and climb out of the plane. Icy fingers of fear criss-crossed the insides of her chest and stomach, constricting her to the point where she didn't think she could breathe.

He appeared at the door of the pavilion and moved to her side. She knew from the look in his eyes what to expect even as she said a silent prayer, *Oh, no, dear God, please no.* Tiny lines of pain formed at the sides of his gray eyes as he reached over to take both her hands in his.

"My uncle?" she choked out the words.

"Kitten, he's collapsed and has been taken to the hospital. Willy thinks he may have had a heart attack."

"No, no, no," she repeated over and over, half to herself and half in a whisper.

He gathered her into his strong arms and hugged her to him. "Honey, Matt is a tough one. I know he will be all right."

She pulled back to look at him, dazed for a moment at the powerful feelings that engulfed her. Her Uncle Matt was the only family she had left, she loved him. He had to be all right, he had to. "Please take me to him," she said.

Adam nodded, wrapped an arm around her shoulders and led her to his car.

Chapter Six

The hospital waiting room was deserted on this summer afternoon. She sat hunched over on a low couch, staring at the patterned linoleum floor. Vaguely she heard Adam pacing back and forth in front of her. Doctors were paged over the loudspeaker system and occasionally footsteps echoed down the hallway. She did not look up. She stared at the floor in a dazed stupor and waited.

She didn't remember anything about the drive to the hospital except that Adam kept glancing over at her and squeezing the hands that she clasped tightly together on her lap. He didn't try to speak and neither did she.

Her white cotton slacks stuck to her legs and the blue-checked, short-sleeved shirt she wore clung to her back where perspiration had made damp patches. She heard his foot-steps stop their pacing for a moment and then he was back by her side.

"Here, drink this," Adam said in a gentle voice.

She looked up to see him with a Styrofoam cup of water in his hands. Dumbly she reached out and grasped the cup. The cool water slid down her parched throat and for a moment revived her. The waiting continued.

Her thoughts were a jumble of images of her uncle's tired face since she had returned home from her trip. She should have suspected that he was really ill. She shouldn't have let him off without seeing a doctor. How long had this been coming? Had the winery's financial problems been so much of a strain on him that they were finally the cause of his collapse? The questions kept coming.

"Miss Carson?"

She looked up at a balding, gray-haired doctor dressed in a white coat. A plastic tag on his breast pocket identified him as Ronald Graham, M.D. She remembered hearing his name but couldn't place it.

"Your uncle has had a heart attack. It was not a severe one, but at the same time heart attacks of any degree are serious business."

"Will he be okay?" She choked out the words.

"We are going to try to make sure of that," he said, a slight smile flitting across his very serious face. "He will need complete rest for a while but there is no reason why he should not make a complete recovery."

The slender thread that had been holding her composure together snapped with those words and tears began coursing down her cheeks. "I'll wait here until I can see him. Is Doctor Loffer here?"

"No, I'm sorry, he's on vacation. I'm his replacement and also his partner." He looked closer at her tear-streaked face and then added, "It may be some time yet, but I'll have the nurse notify you when you can go in for a few minutes."

She nodded her thanks and sat down again. The doctor turned and walked away and an arm was drawn around her shoulders and a white handkerchief pressed into her hands. She looked up at Adam's face as he sat down beside her and saw the strain of the day etched unmistakably across it.

She daubed her wet cheeks and eyes. Her hair made a honey-colored curtain around her face as she bent her head and dried her tears. Then she looked up at Adam again. "He did say he would be all right?"

He reached over and pushed the hair back over her shoulders and then gathered her into his arms. "Yes, he did, Kitten. He is going to make it." His hand stroked the back of her head gently, comforting her as if she were a young child.

Slowly she began to relax and allow the

gentle stroking and the strength of his arms to comfort her. She remembered another time when she was very young and her world had come crashing down around her. Then she had cried alone, in the dark, with no one to comfort her. Now, strong arms held her fast, and the fear slowly receded.

She sat back and pulled herself free. "I need to call Willy, she will be worried sick."

He nodded silently and drew her to her feet. "Honey, I'll stay for as long as you and Matt need me."

"Thank you, Adam," she replied, still numb with shock at what had happened and unable to think clearly about the implications of his statement. She went to look for a telephone.

The day dragged on, and from time to time she would approach the desk to inquire how her uncle was doing, only to be told, "He's resting comfortably."

Adam urged her to eat something and offered to go to a nearby restaurant and bring back some food but she refused. The thought of having food in her mouth was unappealing. He stayed with her all day, alternately holding her hand in his and bringing her cups of water. It was early evening when a nurse came over to where they were sitting.

"Miss Carson, the doctor says you may see your uncle for a few minutes."

She leaped up and followed her down a long corridor. This was what she had been waiting for. She had to see him, to know that he was all right. She had to see him with her own eyes. Her parents had simply disappeared from her life that terrible day long ago and she had never seen them again. She had not gone to the funeral and she had only a few photographs tucked away in her dresser drawer and vague memories.

Tom had also disappeared from her life in one flaming moment. She had been too numb to remember much of anything after she heard the news.

As they approached the door the nurse said, "He will probably be asleep so don't be alarmed if he doesn't open his eyes."

She nodded and went in.

For a long time afterwards she would remember the awesome sight of her uncle lying in the hospital bed, hooked up to various machines, as still as death. Her initial reaction was that they had lied, that he was going to die. But as she moved closer to the bed he opened his eyes briefly, and she smiled and gave his hand a gentle squeeze.

Later, as she thought about it, it was in that moment that she truly believed what the doctor had told her. Her uncle's eyes had said it all, "I'm strong, Kit, and I'm going to be around for a long time." And she had believed him.

She felt a shuddering relief as she walked back down the corridor to the waiting room and allowed herself to be persuaded to return home.

The days that followed fell into a routine of hospital visits and working in the retail shop. As word spread throughout the valley, the telephone rang daily with inquiries from friends and offers of help. Adam stepped into running the winery with an ease that surprised her. He took over almost at once and began supervising the summer work and preparing for the harvest.

Gradually the time she was allotted to visit her uncle increased as his condition improved, and soon he was sitting up talking to her and Willy or Adam and opening the cards and letters that poured in daily from his friends. Johnny came one day and poked his head in the door for a few minutes.

She restricted herself and the others to light conversation and pleasantries during the hospital visits. Now more than ever it was important that he not be troubled by worrying about the winery. As a result the question underlying all of the pleasant banter was not discussed. The winery was left in the shadows during those early days of recovery.

He never asked the question that she knew must occur to him from time to time. What would happen now? Adam had taken over, he knew that, and she assured him that things were running smoothly. The truth was that she had no idea how things were going because Adam was so busy preparing for the harvest and studying the company books that she scarcely saw him.

She knew he had gotten to know some of the other winery owners in the valley and that they were helping him with all of the resources which they could spare. Judging by appearances, everything seemed to be going along on schedule.

Finally the day came when her uncle was allowed to return home. Kit sat in the ambulance with him and joked about his lord-of-the-manner homecoming as they made their way up the steep hill to the house. When he was carefully tucked in his bed in the downstairs guest room, Willy fussed around him making sure he was comfortable. Kit went upstairs to her bedroom and lay down for a few moments to rest. The worry and strain of the past few weeks had taken their toll on her. She fell into a deep sleep and did not awaken until evening.

As the summer days passed and her uncle grew stronger she was aware of the fact that Adam still stayed in the background most of the time. He had stopped pressing her to trust him since the heart attack and now allowed her to spend her time with her uncle without interruption. Although he ate his dinner with them, he was quieter than he had been when he had first come to their house, as if he were watching and waiting for the right time to make his thoughts known.

The grapes were ripening on the vines and their fragrant smell filled the valley. The harvest would begin in September and Kit knew from the many harvests that she had experienced before that it would be a busy time. They would hire extra help to pick the grapes from the Silverado-owned vineyards, but because their acreage was small, they purchased additional grapes from other growers in the valley, and soon large trucks would lumber up the hill, filled with their precious cargo.

But before any of the grapes were picked, the equipment must be spotlessly clean. She remembered in the past how the gondolas which held the grapes, the crusher and the press were always scrubbed down by her uncle in the summer. The stainless steel tanks which held the fermenting wine had to be washed down and sterilized as well.

All of this summer work Adam was supervising with locally hired help. He chatted with her uncle in the evenings but she knew Adam kept these meetings brief so as not to tire him out.

As she lay in bed one evening she worried about the conversation she had had with her uncle just before dinner. He had visited the doctor that day and was told that he was making excellent progress.

"Adam is doing such a good job that soon I won't be needed at all," he joked.

"You are the backbone of the winery, Uncle

Matt, no one will ever take your place," she had asserted firmly.

His fingers raked his rumpled gray hair. "Kit, I owe him so much. The way he's taken over the running of the winery since my heart attack, you'd think he . . ."

"Owned the place," she had finished for him.

"Well, at least half of it. If I hadn't had my heart attack we'd probably have finished our talks."

Kit had not been able to let him finish. The conversation had become too serious. "I think you should put this aside for now. When you are completely well we can discuss it further. Adam is managing now."

"Yes, he is and it is a relief in a way not to have to worry about things."

She looked at him sharply, wondering if his spirit had been broken by the heart attack. Surely he couldn't give up so easily. But she said nothing and the conversation was allowed to turn to other subjects.

Now, twisting and turning in bed, she could not forget the look on his face. It was as if Adam had already bought him out and he was just an interested onlooker. It had taken him a lifetime to build the winery and she could imagine him selling out to Adam Redmont in a moment of weakness and regretting it later. She would not allow that to happen. Selling out would break his spirit and then what would happen to his health? She shuddered, unwilling to follow where that trail of thought led.

The warmth of her room and her tortuous twistings and turnings left her unable to sleep. She decided finally to get up and go downstairs for a cool drink. A shaft of moonlight illuminated her room, so she felt no need to turn on the light as she slid her feet to the floor and reached for a thick cotton robe to cover her transparent nightgown. Then she changed her mind. It was warm enough without the robe and everyone would surely be asleep by now. She would only be downstairs a few minutes, anyway.

The stairwell was dark but she did not wish to awaken anyone, least of all her uncle, so she did not switch on the lights but rather tiptoed, barefoot, downstairs.

She made her way across the kitchen and reached the refrigerator door. Pulling it open, she blinked as the light hit her eyes. A small pitcher of juice was visible behind a jar of pickles and she bent down to reach it. A single sound made her stop her fumbling and turn around. Adam stood in the doorway of the kitchen.

"What are you doing down here in the middle of the night, Kitten?"

She knew she had made a mistake about the robe as she stood in the darkened kitchen with the light coming from the refrigerator behind her illuminating her thinly clad body. "I couldn't sleep so I came down here for something cold to drink. Sorry to disturb you." She turned back to the refrigerator and heard him walk across the kitchen floor and stop right behind her.

"Oh, you disturb me. You can be sure of that."

The huskiness in his voice caused her to turn around again and she felt a tremor of excitement go through her at what she saw. He must have been getting ready for bed when he heard her in the kitchen, for he was wearing blue denim slacks and his chest was bare. Dark curly hairs covered his muscular chest, tapering to a V at his belt line and the sheer male presence of him made her heart beat faster and a strange tension invade her body.

"I'll just pour my juice and take it upstairs," she said, hoping she sounded calm.

"You've been busily hurrying away from me for the last few weeks, haven't you?" His hands were on her shoulders and he was turning her around to face him.

"That's not true. You're the one who's been busy and besides my . . . my uncle needed me," she said, mentally cursing herself for sounding like a frightened teen-ager.

"Ah yes, your uncle. Does he need you now, Kitten?" he asked quietly.

"Please let me go," she whispered, afraid that if she stayed any longer she would fall under the spell of those treacherous hands and not want to leave at all.

"Why are you afraid of me?"

"I'm not afraid," she replied.

He smiled a slow smile, the kind that reached to the depths of his smoky eyes. "Then let yourself go," he whispered, "I won't hurt you."

She longed to let herself go, to give herself to him and forget her suspicions. Could she believe that she wouldn't be hurt as she had been hurt before?

He didn't wait for her to answer but drew her gently toward him until she could feel the hairs on his chest through the sheer gown as they brushed her soft breasts. And then slowly, deliberately he put his lips to hers.

His kiss was a gentle pressure against her lips and she responded by parting them for him without thinking. Then she was enveloped in a passionate embrace as he held her tightly against him, caressing her back and her hips while he rained kisses across her face.

The fire which she tried to quench burned hotter and hotter and she responded fully by wrapping her arms around his neck and kissing him back with abandon. Her fingers slid into the thick black curls as she pressed herself against him.

Before she knew what was happening the straps of her gown were pushed aside and he was kissing the pulsing cord of her neck. His lips moved lower until they reached the gentle swell of her breast. She moaned in delight as he cupped them in his hands and brought her swelling buds to pebble hardness with his tongue.

"Adam," she said, her breathing hard and heavy.

"You're right my sweet," he responded, reading her thoughts, his voice raw with emotion. "This is not the time nor the place for me to make love to you properly."

He swept her into his arms and closed the refrigerator with his elbow. Then he stepped quickly through the darkened kitchen and walked to the stairwell. She was so surprised by his actions that she couldn't speak to tell him that she had no intention of letting him make love to her.

They entered her uncle's study and he set her gently on her feet and then flipped on the small desk lamp. She stood silently, trying to calm her nerves.

He closed the door and then turned to her. "Don't look so frightened, I haven't brought you here to finish what I started in the kitchen."

She willed her breathing to return to its normal rate. "Then what did you bring me in here for?"

"Just relax a minute. I want to talk to you.

She stood facing him, wondering if she would ever be able to relax in his presence, especially when all he had to do was touch her to send her heart racing and fingers of fire shooting through her body.

"What was it you wanted to talk to me about?"

He came toward her and took her hands in his. "I want to talk to you about your uncle, the winery and us," he said.

"I hardly think that the middle of the night in my uncle's study is the time or the place for that kind of conversation, do you?"

"No, I don't. But we've both been so busy lately that when I heard you come downstairs I thought I could get you to agree to have dinner with me tomorrow night and then we could talk, privately."

"My uncle . . ."

"Willy is taking good care of Matt."

She had to admit he was right. Whenever she poked her head into his room, Willy was sitting by his bedside talking to him or feeding him. Willy walked in the garden with him and, under her expert care, he seemed to have lost the gaunt, white appearance that he had when he came home from the hospital. But to have dinner with Adam meant that she would have to be alone with him for a lot longer than she was sure she would be able to handle.

She realized now that he might be playing with her but she also knew if she let herself go she could be very serious about him. He affected her as no man had ever done. A smile flitted across her face as it occurred to her that she was showing the caution that her uncle had tried to teach her many years ago. Strangely enough she did not think he would be particularly pleased if he knew.

"Do I take it your smile means that you will accept my dinner invitation?"

"Look, Adam, we really have nothing to talk about. Your business is with my uncle, he owns the winery not me. He's not in any shape to talk business right now so couldn't it wait until after the harvest?"

His lips tightened as he released her hands. "It can't wait and I don't want to talk to your uncle, I want to talk to you. It will be strictly business, if that's what you want."

What could she say. She did not want her uncle to worry or be anymore concerned about the business of the winery than he already was. At least by having dinner with Adam she could discover what he had in mind so that her uncle would be able to enjoy some relatively untroubled days until he was well enough to resume his work.

"Okay, I'll have dinner with you, a business dinner. I have to lead a tour tomorrow so I won't be ready until after six-thirty."

"That will be fine, Kitten. It will be business that we will talk about, unfinished business," he said, a trace of amusement in his voice. "You'd better go back upstairs now because seeing you standing there like that makes talking business the farthest thing from my mind."

She saw his glance go from her neck to her

bare feet and then linger at her breasts, barely concealed by the thin gown.

She moved to the doorway. "Good night, Adam."

He was staring at her as she opened the door but she did hear him murmur good night under his breath. Forgetting the reason she came downstairs in the first place, she went quickly to her room and got into bed.

It was then that she remembered the last part of what he wanted to talk about. He had said "us" as if it were of equal importance with the other business he had mentioned. Was there really an "us" to discuss, or did he just want her, as any attractive man wants a woman? What will happen, she wondered, when he finally gets the winery? Will there still be an "us" to discuss?

She closed her eyes but it was a long time before sleep finally came.

Chapter Seven

$\mathcal{T}$he tour bus pulled up in front of the retail shop after lunch the next day. Kit could hardly call the few hours she had lain in bed *resting,* but she made an effort to look refreshed by showering, putting on a soft blue cotton shirt-waist dress and brushing her hair into a tiny chignon at the back of her head. As she heard the bus arrive she went outside to greet the group of women who had journeyed from the San Francisco area for a day of touring some of the Napa Valley wineries.

Kit usually enjoyed leading groups on tours of the winery because she was proud of her uncle's accomplishments and of the history that was so unique to this area. Today her spirits flagged as she stepped inside the bus and directed it up Whistler Mountain.

Why had she ever agreed to go out to dinner with Adam? She must have been out of her mind. He probably knew she would fight him if he tried to buy her uncle out totally and was going to make a big effort to win her over. Then once he had what he wanted he would drop her and turn to other conquests.

Still, there was nothing but her own suspicions to back up this fear. Suspicions that she had cast aside the day they went soaring but which had come back as she cared for her uncle during his convalescence and watched the way Adam took over every facet of the winery's operation. That evening's dinner was not going to be easy. The attraction he held for her made her forget her uncle, the winery and every bit of pride she possessed when he began to kiss her. She would have to keep him at arm's length, that would be the only way to find out what he was really after.

The bus stopped in front of the winery and she stepped out first, greeting each of the women climbing down from the bus with a few words and a smile.

"Welcome to Silverado Winery. We are a small winery by Napa Valley standards but we have a history that goes back to the end of the last century. Our name comes from a mining town that once existed in this area and that Robert Louis Stevenson described in his story 'Silverado Squatters.' "

This was the part she loved, talking about the history of the area and telling how Silverado was founded. She always began with the Napa Indians that had populated the valley long ago and their colorful tribal names like the Ouluke and the Mayacamas. She liked to tell how no one really knows what the word *Napa* meant to the Indians but people thought it probably translated to "plenty" or "abundant" and most likely referred to the Napa River that was plentiful with fish.

The group followed her as she walked from the bus to the entrance to the stone caves that had been cut into the mountain many years ago by Chinese laborers working for as little as twenty-five cents a day. She told the story of the Frenchman who quarreled with his father about grape growing in his native country and came to America so that he could do things his own way.

"He was attracted to this area because of the long growing season and good soil. He purchased many acres of vineyards in the valley and bought the winery from a German sea captain who had decided to settle down and make wine but who did not have the know-how to make it pay."

She warmed to her subject and forgot her earlier worries as she traced the Frenchman's bad luck with phylloxera, a root louse that spread through the area in the early 1880s.

"Finally, it was discovered that American root stock was resistant to phylloxera and vineyards were saved when planters began to graft European vines to American root stock.

The winery changed ownership many times after the Frenchman died leaving no heirs and it fell into disrepair."

"Now we'll go into the caves and you'll notice how cool they are. This natural cooling system allows us to store wine while it is aging. It is a wine cellar cooled by Mother Nature." Her uncle had had the caves shored up with concrete so there would be no danger of collapse as the workers transported oak and redwood barrels in and out of them.

She told the group about when she was young and she hid behind a huge barrel filled with red wine. Her uncle, an even-tempered man, had become worried about her and started a search party around the winery. When he found her he pulled her out by the scruff of her neck and bellowed in rage at the scare she had given him. For a long time afterwards she was forbidden to go into the caves.

"But he gave me permission today," she added, smiling, and the group broke into delighted laughter.

She led them from the caves to the huge barnlike structure where the grapes were unloaded from giant hoppers and dumped into stem crushers, which popped them off their stems and broke their skins.

As she talked about the process of turning grape juice into wine a movement at the back of the crowd caught her eye. Standing in a darkened corner near one of the stainless steel fermenting tanks, Adam was listening to her tell about wine making. Maybe he was checking up on her, seeing how well she did her job.

A brief anger flared up inside her. Did he think she didn't know her subject? She would show him. She led the group to the press and began an elaborate explanation of how presses were needed to extract juice which did not run freely from the crushing. She explained that white wine grapes were pressed before fermentation began, whereas red wine grapes were pressed afterwards so that the solids and skins would give the wine a red color as well as other desirable characteristics.

They moved to the fermenting tanks and she looked over to see that he had disappeared. She found that, with him gone, she lost some of her enthusiasm for the talk and so shortened the rest of her story.

After the tour the group piled back into the bus and proceeded to the retail shop. There Lisa had set out a counterful of glasses and she and Kit began pouring small portions of Silverado wine and showing the tour group how to sniff the wonderful fresh fruity aroma of the wine before tasting it.

The din of laughter filled the shop as the women enjoyed the tastes of wine and wandered around chatting, looking at the displays and selecting wine for purchase. A person could spend a day in the wine country touring and wine tasting and spending no money for the privilege. Some years before, a winery had tried to charge for tasting and though a few still did it, the idea didn't catch on, for winemakers decided that tasting was a form of advertising. The next time this group found the Silverado label in a store, they would remember their tour and probably make a purchase.

When they filed out the door and onto the bus, Kit realized that she had gotten over one hurdle that day but had a more difficult one that would challenge her that night. She came back after seeing the tour bus off and began taking handfuls of empty wine glasses into the storeroom to wash.

"Kit, Adam called when you were outside. He asked me to tell you that he will be a little late taking you out to dinner. He had to go into Napa and will not be back until seven."

Kit nodded and mumbled her thanks. She did not want Lisa to think that any more than a business relationship existed between her and Adam. After the barbecue she had noticed that Lisa had become more outgoing, taken her hair out of the unbecoming bun and brushed it until it lay flatteringly smooth on her shoulders. Had Adam turned his charm on her, too? Was Lisa jealous of the dinner date? She looked over at the other girl. Lisa's manner was friendly and her look as she gathered up more of the empty wine glasses held nothing but mild curiosity.

The cleanup following the large tour and tasting took up the rest of the afternoon and it was after five when she and Lisa were finally able to lock up.

"I hope you enjoy your dinner," Lisa said as they departed.

Kit thought she sounded genuine, not the least bit jealous or upset. "Thanks," was all she could bring herself to reply.

She puzzled over this as she stood in the shower later, feeling the warm spray of water run down the length of her body. She had been so busy with her uncle for the past weeks that she had scarcely a thought for Lisa and the retail shop. She had attributed Lisa's new self-confidence to Adam, yet she had not seen them together since the night of the Angelli barbecue. Maybe she was mistaken. Perhaps Lisa had another boyfriend.

She towelled herself dry and then stood in front of her closet deciding what to wear. The evening would be warm but she had no intention of exposing her bare shoulders to Adam's gaze or his touch again. She would look demure and businesslike. He did say that they would talk business and she would give him no cause to think she was prepared to do anything else.

She selected a brandy-colored crepe blouse with a matching skirt. The blouse buttoned at the neck in an old-fashioned style and she brushed her hair smooth and then piled it on top of her head to complete the look. She knew she was early but she would have time to visit with her uncle before Adam returned.

She had reached the hallway when the telephone rang. Stepping quickly to the small table in the hall she lifted the receiver.

"Hello?"

"May I speak to Adam Redmont," a female voice asked in a half question, half command.

"I'm sorry, he isn't in right now. May I tell him you called?"

"That won't be necessary," the caller said in a tight clipped voice and hung up.

Kit stood for a moment still holding the receiver. She remembered the maroon suit at the airport. She had heard her only briefly call Adam's name, yet she had the feeling that this woman on the telephone was the same person she had seen.

She put the telephone down and slowly descended the stairs. It was no business of hers if his girlfriends called him, no business at all. Yet, why did she feel a sick ache in the pit of her stomach right now? *Damn him anyway. Damn all handsome men.*

Her knock on the library door brought a muffled "Come in" from her uncle.

Opening the door she found him sitting in his favorite easy chair with Willy hovering over him.

"Is anything wrong?" she asked alarmed.

"No, Kit, everything is fine," he assured her with a strange smile on his face. Willy said nothing but returned the smile and silently left the room.

She took a seat across from him and began

telling him about the tour that day. He listened quietly, but she had the feeling that he was not as interested as he usually was in the groups that visited the winery. Puzzled, she finished her story and leaned over asking, "You're not worrying about anything are you?"

"No, honey, I can honestly say that I've never felt more relaxed in my life."

"Good, you'll be back soon doing what you love."

"Hmmm," was all he said and nodded thoughtfully.

She thought of his lack of enthusiasm strange and glanced over at his body resting comfortably in the chair. He looked trim and fit and she had to admit his face, lined by many years of hard work, was peaceful.

"May I come in?"

Adam filled the doorway with his powerful body. He was wearing chocolate-colored slacks and a creamy silk shirt that contrasted sharply with his dark hair and made him look even more masculine and attractive than he had in the kitchen the night before. He greeted her uncle and told him he was taking Kit out to dinner.

"Good, she deserves some fun. Stuck in this house with me every night is not good for a young person."

"You know I always enjoy spending time with you," she said and was about to add that this was a business dinner but Adam's hand was at her elbow and he was already ushering her from the room.

It was a warm evening. As they walked to his car she began to wonder if her covered-up look was going to mean she would be sweltering all night. He held the car door open and as she got in she caught the aroma of aftershave mixed with the pure male scent of him. This was going to be hard, she thought, very hard to sit and act businesslike when she wanted to ask him what other female was calling him and at the same time run her hands through his black curly hair.

He got in and studied her carefully. "You look like some of the old photos I have of my grandmother," he said, a teasing grin on his face.

She had worked herself up into such a nervous state that the comment stung. "You said this was going to be a business dinner, however if you prefer not to go," she said angrily and moved to open the door but his hand shot out and stopped her.

"My kitten is bristling tonight. Relax, my grandmother is a very attractive woman. What I was telling you was that it is a shame to cover up your beautiful body with all those clothes."

She let go of the door handle and he released her hand. As he withdrew his arm he brushed his sleeve across her crepe-covered breasts. She forced herself to remember the phone call and made herself ignore the warm tingling sensation that his touch aroused. She tried to change the subject. "Where are we going?"

He started the car and swung it around the driveway. "Someplace I discovered on my last trip out here," he answered mysteriously.

She noticed that when he reached the bottom of the hill he turned north onto the highway instead of south where all of the familiar restaurants were located. She decided she had better get a firm grip on herself for this evening. She sat quietly, watching the scenery of vineyards interspersed with houses and farms. Every house had some acreage planted in grapes and the even rows of plants tied to stakes lined both sides of the highway. She sat back and rested her head against the headrest. She had no idea where he was taking her. At one point she noticed that they were climbing into the foothills of the Mayacamas. It was funny, she reflected, she had lived in this valley most of her life and thought she knew every inch of it yet he seemed to have found a restaurant in a place where she had thought none existed. And that while out here on a business trip.

They turned sharply onto a dirt road, creating a shower of dust behind them and drew up in front of what looked like a farmhouse. Other cars were parked in front of it, too, and then Kit realized why Adam had brought her out here. The farmhouse had been turned into a country restaurant. When they entered she saw that in each corner of the living room were small tables covered with lace tableclothes and decorated with wooden candlesticks and delicate glowing tapers. The elegant oak dining room of the farmhouse also contained small tables, with fresh flowers in tiny vases in the center of each table. A crystal chandelier gleamed overhead.

She looked around at the antique furniture and hook rugs on the hardwood floor and thought how much it reminded her of her home. They were ushered to a table in the far corner of the living room where rich brocade draperies and softer wispy sheers fell gently in front of a side window. She was surprised that she was not handed a menu.

"This is a family-owned restaurant and there is one specialty of the house each evening. Tonight it is braised beef ribs. I hope you like them."

"That will be fine. Perhaps we can get down to business now," she replied.

"No, Kitten. Let's enjoy our dinner first."

A pink-cheeked young girl in a starched white apron brought them their salad and Kit resigned herself to a delay before they would begin their business discussion. Adam began telling her how he had discovered the farmhouse one day as he drove around lost and trying to find a gas station.

She listened, amused by the tale, and had to admit to herself that the food was delicious.

The salad was followed by braised ribs covered with thick rich savory gravy and served with fresh garden peas and oven-baked potatoes. Flaky homemade rolls added to the meal and the glass of Cabernet Sauvignon, that Adam kept refilling, at the side of her plate soon relaxed her.

He kept the conversation light, telling her about his own family and showing an obvious affection for his mother and father. He questioned her gently about her early days with her uncle and under the influence of the homey atmosphere and several glasses of wine she found herself relaxing even more and telling him what little she could remember about her own parents.

When slices of homemade pie were placed on the table, she groaned. "I don't think I can eat another thing."

"Taste it," he said, looking at her with amused tolerance.

She did and it was heavenly.

"You don't eat enough, you know that. You look as if a good wind would blow you away."

"Willy has been trying to fatten me up for years," she laughed, finishing the pie.

She looked over at him and saw that he was watching her with his silvery eyes, and his intent gaze had a disturbing effect. To cover the warm heady feeling that rippled through her, she asked, "Can we get down to business, now?"

"Oh, yes, we musn't forget business," he mocked softly.

"That's why we came isn't it?"

He didn't answer the question but instead sat back in his chair and let his eyes roam over her face. She found this disturbing and could barely control her impatience as she sat waiting for him to speak.

"Your uncle has asked me to buy him out, Kitten," he said finally.

"No!" she said, shocked. She couldn't believe it. Surely he would have told her. She flashed back on the conversation that had taken place earlier that evening between her uncle and herself. The expression on his face should have warned her that something was not right. Lifting her chin defiantly, she said, "He has no choice, his expenses have gotten too great and now with his heart attack he'll have to cut back on his work."

"Maybe he does have a choice and that is what he's chosen."

"I'll never believe that. The winery has meant so much to him. He's worked terribly hard over the years to get it going and keep it going. I'll never believe he would choose to sell it if he didn't have to."

"It means a lot to you, too, doesn't it?"

"Of course it does. It's the only life I've ever known."

"And you're not sure what you'll do if your uncle doesn't own the winery?"

The question was neatly phrased and asked very quietly but the implications of what he was asking seared Kit's brain. He thought she couldn't let go of the winery because of her own selfish interests. She glared at him, a swift anger rising in her.

"If you are implying that I am the one who needs the winery, you are very much mistaken."

"Am I? You gave a tour today and you relished every moment of it."

"Of course I enjoyed it, I always do. You didn't need to spy on me to find that out," she said angrily.

She saw a muscle twitch along the side of his jaw.

"Let's get out of here," he said suddenly, pulling some money from his pocket, tossing it on the table and ushering her from the room.

They drove in silence to a hillside where the whole valley spread before them in silence. Tiny lights flickered from the towns far away and the air was thick with the intoxicating sweet smell of the grapes, this was Silverado land. The carefully tended vines burgeoning with grapes would soon yield their harvest.

He opened the door and drew her out to stand with him, looking over the quiet valley. "You love this," he said. "You might as well admit it, Kitten, you love this land and this way of life as much as your uncle does."

He came up to stand behind her. His hands

slipped around her waist and his breath ruffled her hair.

"Yes, I do. I love it, my uncle loves it, what does that prove? A man doesn't give up everything he's worked for without good reason."

"That's just the point. A near brush with death could cause a man to rearrange his priorities."

"What do you mean?" she turned to face him.

"I can't explain Matt to you, but I know that now he seems eager to sell out and move on to another way of life. I've noticed the change coming gradually as we've talked in the evenings. He's mused over the work that needs to be done and how he should be helping out but he'd also talked about the fact that he is getting on in years and won't be able to do this forever."

"I don't believe you. Why didn't he tell me if that was what he wanted?"

He sighed. "I don't expect you to believe me. Talk to him, find out if what I say is true."

His hands rested on her shoulders. Those treacherous hands were pulling her gently toward him.

"No!" she said, suddenly pulling away. "You're telling me this so it will be easier for you to do what you intended doing from the beginning, neutralize the opposition."

"So we're back to that again." His voice was low and his hands were reaching for the pins that held her hair.

"Don't touch me!"

It was as if his thin rein of control on his emotions suddenly snapped with her outburst. He reached out and pulled her to him with bruising swiftness and savagely brought his lips down on hers. It was not so much a kiss as it was a mark of possession. She had no time to think, no time to draw back, only time to feel. His lips came down hard and demanding and his arms held her in a grip of steel. Then abruptly everything changed.

As if her shock and surprise halted his suddenly emotional reaction, his savagery gave way to gentleness that devastated her. He held her firmly as his lips plundered her face. Gentle teasing kisses fell on her eyelids, her cheeks and her lips.

She tried to remain passive under the onslaught but found his gentleness harder to ignore than his strength. Her traitorous body clamored for the feel of him against her. With a sigh she slid her arms around his neck and pressed her lips to his.

His fingers at last found the pins holding her hair and quickly discarded them. He held handfuls of her soft hair in his hands and kissed them.

"I've been wanting to do this all night," he groaned.

The warmth of the evening and the warmth that was building up between them was more than Kit could stand in her buttoned-up crepe blouse. She reached to unbutton the two top buttons so that she could breathe easier.

"Let me help," he murmured, fumbling with the next two buttons.

"Can't you think of anything else?" she asked, her voice sounding oddly shaken to her own ears.

"Not when I'm with you." His voice was husky as he kissed the base of her neck where her throbbing pulse was exposed. "I want you, Kitten."

Not, I love you, she thought. But, I want you, as he wants other women and as he wants the winery.

"No, please, I want to go home," she said, pulling from his grasp.

"When are you going to admit that you want me as much as I want you? Whatever your former husband did is over and done with, you can't put a barricade up in front of your feelings and hide yourself in a winery all of your life."

"I can do anything I like. It's none of your business."

"Don't be too sure about that, Green-Eyes," he said pulling her back into his arms. "I told you I want you and I'm going to have you."

"You are one of the most arrogant men I've ever met. Can't you understand that I don't want you," she said angrily, pulling out of his grasp.

"Your body sends out a different message

every time I touch you, but pride or mistrust or something stands in the way. God help me if I know what it is."

"I just don't happen to fall at your feet like all your other conquests," she shot back. She was on the verge of telling him about the phone call but something made her control her tongue. She knew that whatever she told him he would turn to his own advantage.

"All the other women, hell," he said angrily. "Something has gotten your dander up; what is it?"

"You want the winery, well you're not going to get it." She was yelling at him in the quiet darkness of the hillside, unable to stop herself.

He laughed, a hard brittle laugh. "How are you going to stop me?"

It was his laugher, his humiliating laughter that finally pushed her over the brink. "I'm going to marry Johnny Angelli."

"You're what?" he asked harshly.

"Johnny has asked me to marry him and I intend to accept," she replied.

"You crazy little idiot. Do you think that marrying him will change anything? You and I set sparks off in each other because we belong together. Even Angelli can see that."

"I want to go home."

He swore under his breath and opened the car door. "Get in," he said harshly.

The drive home was strained and tense. Not a word was spoken between them, but the atmosphere was electrically charged. As they pulled into the driveway and he switched off the engine, she made a move to get out of the car.

"Oh, no, you don't," he said pulling her around to face him. "I have agreed to stay on and help your uncle with the harvest and we will begin the legal work necessary for him to sell the winery. What you've told me tonight won't make any difference."

"Yes it will," she answered angrily. "Do you think my uncle will sell out to you knowing that I'm going to be in a position to buy the winery myself?"

"I think your uncle will do what's fair and what is best. As for your crazy scheme to marry Johnny Angelli, my God, even he'll see that you are making a big mistake."

"I'm not interested in what you think. Now, please let me go."

He released her and said in a low voice, I'll never let you go, Kit, never."

She opened the car door and got out. Nothing in the world would make her look back now.

Chapter Eight

*A*fterward she wondered why she'd said it. She had not intended to and she supposed it was being backed into a corner that was part of the reason she told him she was going to marry Johnny. The other part of it she knew was the phone call. He was still seeing other women, although he professed to be enamored with her. No, she corrected herself, he never said that, he had only said he wanted me.

Well, Tom had wanted her once and then had stopped wanting her and went on to wanting someone else. She was not going to let that happen to her again and she was not going to let him get control of the winery.

She told Johnny the next day. Slipping out

of the house early in the morning, she drove over to the Angelli house and found him out in the vineyards. She tried to shut out the memory of the tall, powerful body as she gazed at the slim, lean lines of Johnny Angelli. So what if he didn't move her the way Adam did, she told herself, here was someone she could trust.

At first, when she told him she accepted his proposal, he seemed stunned. He looked at her in shocked surprise for a moment and then smiled brilliantly, picked her up in his arms and swung her around. Then he kissed her and she knew that his kisses would never cause a flame to ignite her passion but she told herself she didn't need the flame. Passion doesn't last and flames turn to ashes. She did not need that kind of agony again in her life.

He insisted on taking her to the house and telling his parents immediately. Papa and Mama Angelli were of course delighted. They loved Kit and she could see that they felt that marriage to their second son would in some way atone for the disastrous marriage to their eldest.

It was only later, when she drove back to the house to tell her uncle, that she began to feel nervous. She was not sure how he would take the news and she was not sure if he would see through her plan.

He was in the quiet of his study when she returned home and Willy was apparently out grocery shopping. She glanced around to see if she could see Adam over by the winery but he was nowhere around.

Her uncle was sitting in his old-fashioned bentwood rocker, with his cat Chablis curled up in his lap. He took the news calmly, quietly, his hand stroking Chablis gently behind the ears.

"What have you gotten yourself into, Kit?" he asked gently, his eyes probing her face.

"I've just told you, I'm going to marry Johnny," she said, feeling for one moment like the school-age Kit of long ago.

He stared at her silently for a moment. "But why?"

"Why does any girl get married?" she replied.

"You're not any girl and you've been married. You once said he is like a big brother to you."

"Maybe I was wrong about that. I've known him forever and I trust him."

"Yes, he's a good man, better than his brother ever was, but is that enough to make you happy?"

"I will be happy with Johnny," she answered quietly.

"I hope so, Kit. I've learned that you have to live your own life, honey. I love you and if this is what you want, I give you my blessing."

She leaned over and gave him a peck on the cheek. "Thank you, Uncle Matt. I wanted to tell you right away so that whatever plans you have for the winery could be changed."

"The winery? Kit, I'm going to sell it," he paused, letting his statement sink in. "I want to marry Willy and live the rest of my years with her."

"Oh, Uncle Matt," Kit whispered, overcome with emotion. She wrapped her arms around his neck suddenly and gave him a quick hug. Startled, Chablis jumped from his lap. "You and Willy . . . I always thought . . ."

"I didn't know myself. My heart attack changed a lot of things in my life. I started to see what made a difference and what didn't. I've always cared for Willy, since she first came to take care of us. But it was only when I became so very ill that I realized that she was important to me beyond that. I love her and I'm lucky enough that she loves me, too. We want to be married very soon, as soon as I get the okay from the doctor. Every day is precious to me now, Kit, and I don't want to waste one of them. As for the winery, I intended to sell it to Adam and go back to consulting. Now, with you and Johnny getting married . . ."

"Uncle Matt, I haven't discussed this with Johnny but I know that he will want to buy you out if it can be arranged. We could live here and run the winery ourselves."

"Honey, you are my only heir and of course I want you to have Silverado. It's just that I have contractual obligations to Adam right now so that it won't be easy."

"What do you mean?"

"Right after he came here he saw that I needed some things done even before the harvest. He advanced me the money and has an option to buy half interest in the winery. I thought that I would just sell out to him, but now with you and Johnny getting married, of course I won't do that."

"Johnny and I will buy out his half interest if we have to."

"*If* he'll sell, you can. He wants this place, Kit. He's done a good job in running it so far and I think he wants to stay in the wine business. His option to buy was part of the loan and I can't go back on that. Of course, the other half of the business would be for you and Johnny."

Kit took a deep breath, this was going to be harder than she thought. "Maybe he'll change his mind and let his option go."

"Now why should I do that?" a deep voice said from the doorway.

She turned to find him leaning against the frame, his eyes on her and an amused curl to his lips.

"Sorry for eavesdropping, Matt, the door was open. I came to talk to you."

"Come in, Adam, Kit and I have some good news for you."

"Oh?" he said, looking at her pointedly.

"Kit is going to marry Johnny Angelli and I

have had the good fortune to have my proposal accepted by Sara Williams."

"My congratulations to you, Matt. Willy is a fine woman and I know you will be very happy together."

Some perverse deviltry made her ask, "Aren't you going to congratulate me, too?"

He looked over at her, his gray eyes like flinty steel. "You already know my feelings on that subject," he said coolly.

The atmosphere became tense as an uneasy quiet settled on the room after Adam's remark. Kit saw her Uncle Matt look from one to the other of them with a puzzled frown on his face. Finally he said to Adam, "You wanted to talk to me?"

Kit decided that this was the moment to excuse herself. She had had enough of Adam's company the night before. She murmured a few words to her uncle and, as she turned to leave, Adam inclined his head as if to say, the battle's been launched, we'll see who the winner will be.

She glared back at him and then walked out of the room, closing the door behind her. She stood in the hallway and breathed a sigh of relief. She knew now that he would make her life very difficult but she was determined to see her plan through to the end.

That night she treated Willy and her uncle to a home-cooked meal, cooked entirely by herself. Adam was absent, so the three of them celebrated their upcoming marriages by laughing and talking and sharing memories of old times. Willy beamed with happiness at her forthcoming marriage every time she looked over at Matt Carson and Kit was glad for them. She was aware that she was not beaming and radiant as she should be but if anyone else noticed it, they kept the fact to themselves.

Angie, however, had not been so polite. Kit had driven over earlier to tell her the news and found her best friend was not easily deceived.

"Why are you doing this, Kit?"

"Why does any girl get married? Why did you?" she replied.

"You know it isn't the same thing. You've known Johnny since you were kids and you've always treated him like he was your brother as well as mine. What made you decide to marry him?"

"Maybe I decided it was time to get married again. Maybe your announcement gave me the push I needed to start thinking of settling down and raising a family." She smiled gamely but knew she was not fooling Angie one bit.

"Does Adam Redmont have anything to do with this?"

"Why should he?"

"Because the way you were looking at each other at the barbecue I thought there might be something between you two."

"The only thing that's between us is the

winery. Adam wants it and I intend that he isn't going to get it."

"Kit, I'm glad you've come out of your depression over Tom and are considering marrying again. But I'm not sure Johnny is right for you anymore than Tom was."

"Angie, I . . ."

"No, hear me out," she said gesturing with her open hand. "I love you as if you were my own sister and I feel partly responsible for what happened between you and Tom. After all, I introduced you, or reintroduced you, that day he started chasing after you. Deep in my heart I knew what kind of a person my own brother was. Now I have a chance to keep you from making another mistake."

"Angie, I hardly think you ought to warn me off Johnny, he's not like Tom."

"That's just the point. He's steady and responsible and he's all the things that Tom wasn't but he still isn't for you, sweet. You need someone strong who can rein in your impulsiveness and love you as Tom never did. Johnny would only idolize you and that is not enough."

"I'm going to marry Johnny, Angie. I will try to make him a good wife. I'm sorry you don't think it's a good idea. I care for him and I trust him," she said, beginning to feel annoyed with her friend.

"It isn't enough, you need to love him as you've never loved anyone in your life," Angie persisted.

Kit did not reply because at that moment the only thought that flashed through her mind was that there was only one man that she could feel that way about but he was merely dallying with her while he dated other women on the side.

After her talk with Angie she found herself visiting Johnny at the Angelli house almost every night. Often Angie and her husband would join them and the four of them would play cards or sit quietly talking and laughing in the summer night. Angie watched her with Johnny but said no more about her thoughts on the marriage.

Johnny bought her an engagement ring, and when he slipped it on her finger and gave her a loving kiss, she knew her fate was sealed. There would be no changing her mind from now on.

It was Lisa who behaved the most strangely, however. From the day she found out about Kit's engagement, she reverted back to her old self. She pulled her hair back in a severe bun and her quiet shyness slipped back into place. After a few weeks Kit had a hard time remembering that for a brief time she had been an outgoing girl with sparkling eyes.

Kit was up early one Sunday morning because Johnny was taking her on a picnic to a nearby lake. The shrill of the telephone ringing broke the silence of the house. She picked it up from the upstairs extension and heard a breathy voice say, "Adam, darling."

"Caroline," he replied.

She realized that he was downstairs on the other phone and quietly hung up the receiver. So that was the name of the brunette who had called him before and was possibly the same woman in the maroon suit who had met him at the airport. While now she knew, in spite of herself she felt a deep-seated agony at knowing. It would have been better if she hadn't found out her name. Then she would be one of the nameless legions that he probably pursued and it wouldn't be so hard to bear.

She brooded about it during the long drive and finally decided to put it to rest. There was nothing to be done. She was engaged to Johnny. He seemed not to notice her quietness in the car, for he was quiet himself. It was not until they were seated on a grassy bank overlooking the lake that they began to talk.

The last remnants of Willy's roast beef sandwiches were gone and Kit munched on a juicy apple. He rested against a tree trunk, a reflective expression on his face. She finished her apple and tucked the core into a paper bag.

"Kit, you do love me, don't you?" he asked suddenly.

She looked over at him and at the solemn expression on his face. "Of course I love you, silly," she said lightly.

"No, its not silly, honey. You told me once you loved me as a brother but now you've agreed to marry me."

"I've known you a long time, Johnny, and I guess I've treated you like a brother because Angie and I are best friends and that's how she's always treated you."

He reached out and pulled her over to him. "This is like a dream come true for me. Ever since we were kids I've thought and planned about our getting married."

What could she say? That it had been her dream, too, when she knew deep down that that was untrue. She sighed, "Johnny."

Misinterpreting her emotions he kissed her passionately while she tried to respond and to put out of her mind the dark-haired man with the gray eyes who had kissed her and whispered, "I want you."

It was much later when they returned home, driving through the twisting roads that circled the vineyards. In the gathering dusk Johnny guided the car up the hill. He has been very quiet on the drive home, she thought. She had tried to draw him out several times but found that though his replies were polite his mind was elsewhere.

He opened the car door for her and helped her out. She saw a light glowing from behind the living room curtains.

"Come in for a minute and say hello to Uncle Matt," she said softly.

"Okay, Kit."

They pushed open the front door and stepped into the hallway. The double doors leading to the living room were closed. Kit quickly walked over and pushed them open, expecting to find her uncle relaxing in his favorite lounge chair. Instead, the open doors revealed Lisa sitting on a low-slung couch with her head resting against Adam's shoulder while he cradled her protectively in his arms. At the sound of the sliding doors they both looked up quickly and Kit caught a glimpse of Lisa's tear-stained face an instant before she buried it again against his shoulder.

"We thought Uncle Matt might be in here, sorry," she murmured, trying to cover the anguish she felt at seeing another woman in his arms.

She turned around and found Johnny standing stock still beneath the hall light. His face was suddenly pale and his hands were jammed into his pants pockets.

"I think I'd better go home, Kit. I'll drop by tomorrow to see you," he said in a strangely harsh voice.

He dropped a brief kiss on her forehead and turned to leave. The sliding doors rumbled back open and Adam stood in the doorway.

"Johnny, would you mind giving Lisa a lift home?" he asked casually, as if nothing had happened.

Kit still felt the pain of seeing her there in

Adam's arms. When Johnny nodded silently in agreement, she watched Adam pull Lisa to her feet and walk with his arm protectively around her shoulders to the front door.

Lisa had dried her tears and put her glasses back on. She looked embarrassed and terribly uncomfortable. Kit knew Adam could be devastating to any woman when he turned on the charm and despite the raging jealousy consuming her she also felt compassion for shy, quiet Lisa Gerard. As the two left and the front door closed, she turned to go upstairs.

"Just a minute, I'd like to speak to you."

He was standing in the empty hallway, looking at her with angry gray eyes and tight lips.

"We have nothing to say to each other," she said and lifted her foot onto the first stair.

At once his hand was on her shoulder and he spun her around to face him. The gray eyes blazed and his powerful body looked ominously large in the lighted hallway.

"I said I'd like to speak to you and damn it I'm going to."

He lifted her off her feet so suddenly she had no chance to draw back. Strong arms carried her back into the living room and dumped her unceremoniously onto the couch.

She lay back, staring in shocked surprise as he went back and closed the doors.

"Matt and Willy have gone to her daughter's house for dinner. So we will not be interrupted."

She recovered her composure and sat up. "Ah yes, the caveman technique," she said sarcastically. "Well, now that I'm here, what is it that you wanted to say?"

He stood over her, his hands in his pockets. "You drive a man to the limits, you know that?"

"I believe, Mr. Redmont, you wished to speak to me about something," she said icily, holding herself in rigid control.

"Yes, I wanted to speak to you, Miss Katherine Amanda Carson, because you are making a damned fool of yourself."

Her anger blazed swiftly, "How dare you."

"Yes, I dare. Somebody's got to make you see that you don't go playing around with people and their feelings."

He sat down on the couch next to her. His face was an angry mask and his jaw tense and tight. She was puzzled at his outburst as well as surprised.

"I don't know what you're talking about," she said, moving to get up, but his hands held her in their forceful grip. "Let go of me," she yelled.

"No, I won't let you run away. You're going to sit here and listen to me if it takes all night."

She realized that he was not going to release her and that no one was going to come to her aid, so she stopped struggling. Sensing her acquiescence he eased his grip on her hands.

"You can't play with other people's feelings," he repeated in a low, somber voice.

"What are you talking about?"

"I'm talking about Johnny and Lisa."

"What about them?" she tilted her head up defiantly.

"They are in love with each other, any fool can see that."

"No, it's not true," she whispered, but at the same time a crazy feeling of relief ran through her. It wasn't Adam and Lisa, it was Lisa and Johnny.

"Oh, yes, you selfish little idiot. Couldn't you see the way she came alive when he was with her at the barbecue and how he looked at her this evening? Are you so wrapped up in your own plans that you didn't notice?"

"You've no right to say such things to me. Of course I didn't notice. Do you think I would have accepted his proposal if I had?"

"I don't know what you do when you get a crazy notion in your head. You didn't want me to have the winery and by marrying Johnny you thought you could guarantee it."

So he knew. Did he also know the dangerous effect he had on her from the very beginning, she wondered.

"You forget," he continued, "I already have an option on half of it. Even if your uncle gave you half for a wedding present, I would still be a partner."

"I thought . . . I, that is, we thought we might be able to persuade you to let the option go." She looked into his face and knew she had made a mistake.

"You thought wrong. I'll never give up my rights to half."

"Don't you mean your company's rights?"

"No, I intend to buy half of this winery with my own money. The company is not involved in any way."

She leaned back against the cushions looking at his unsmiling mouth. She had to ask him. "Why?" she said softly.

"I told you once but you weren't ready to listen, now maybe you are. I've always liked this part of the country. I've spent years traveling around looking for good investments for other people's money but when I saw this valley I knew that this is where I wanted to live and to invest my own."

She looked at him as if she were seeing him for the first time. The anger had drained away and there was something in his eyes that she didn't quite understand.

He continued, "I think you'd better know the whole story, even if Matt doesn't approve. My father loaned your uncle money years ago so that he could send you to school. They met years ago because my father knew your parents."

She stared at him incredulously. "How? When?" she managed to choke out.

"The family business was started in Baltimore by my grandfather. He had four sons and they all went into the business, but my father decided he wanted to work in Virginia, not far from the capital, so that he could open his own branch."

"And Uncle Matt?" she asked, still shaken by what he had told her.

"Matt got in touch with my father when he was settling your parents' estate. When I made my first trip out here I got his address and came to see him."

"I didn't know. I didn't know any of this."

"No, Matt thought it would be better because he felt you wouldn't go to college if you knew he had to borrow money to send you. A few nights ago I intended to ask him if I could tell you the whole story but I never got the chance. I suspected Lisa and Johnny had fallen in love with each other that night of the barbecue. Tonight Lisa came to see me because she was very upset. She didn't see how she could go on working with you when you were marrying the man she loved."

She closed her eyes and sank back against the cushions. This was almost too much to absorb in one evening she thought dully.

"Kitten?" he asked gently.

She opened her eyes and saw that the anger was gone from the gray eyes.

"Your uncle has known my family for a long time. He's not selling because he has been pushed into a corner. He wants to change his life style. Your marrying Johnny to keep the winery in the family is not going to change anything. I'm sorry you had to hear it like this.

I know it must be a shock but it's best that you know the truth."

"Yes, well don't trouble yourself on my account," she said stiffly.

"Oh, but I do," he said and began pulling her to him.

She struggled halfheartedly, the fight as well as the anger gone.

"Why even try? You know this is what you want," he murmured.

He was right. As soon as his lips came down on hers she felt all of the emotions she had kept in check surge through her in one overwhelming wave.

He held her against the cushions while his lips roamed her cheeks and her ears, planting kisses and leaving a trail of fire in their wake. And then slowly he eased her back into the couch and moved his body on top of her. At what point she began responding to his kisses she did not know. She found herself unbuttoning the buttons of his shirt and feeling the muscled hardness of his chest beneath her hands. His heart was beating excitedly, making her aware that he was as moved as she.

He fumbled with her blouse and bra. She gasped in delight when he cupped her breast and his lips teased her rose-tipped nipples to hard peaks.

"Kitten, Kitten," he groaned her name into her ear as he reached for the snap of her slacks.

She was lost to the world of rational

thought, awash in sensations that made her ache with a primitive hunger. His touch drove her to the point of madness. She thought she gasped out his name but the voice was so unlike her own that she wasn't sure. She wanted to give herself completely to the sweet mastery of his hands and his lips.

There was a blinding light. She blinked in confusion as Adam sat up abruptly.

"Matt and Willy are back," he said in a husky voice.

She sat up quickly and put herself back together as he rebuttoned his shirt.

"I shouldn't have done that," he said in a low voice.

She looked at him, confused by his statement. She should have stopped him yet she hadn't, she had wanted him to continue and now, was he regretting it?

"You are engaged to another man," he said simply, reading her thoughts.

And you are in love with another woman, she said silently to herself as she stood up and went to the door.

"We both made a mistake," she said, opening the sliding doors as her uncle and Willy entered the house. She didn't turn back to hear his answer.

Chapter Nine

Johnny called for her early the next morning and took her for a drive. She felt the tension in the air as they sped along the highway and wondered if she should speak first. She knew now what he was going through, yet she decided to let him tell her how he felt before she blurted out anything and spoiled their friendship. That's what they had had all along, friendship, nothing more.

He slowed down and turned onto a dirt road that ran alongside the Angelli vineyards, then stopped the car. She rolled down the window. As early in the morning as it was, the day was already warm.

"Kit, I need to explain about last night," he said quietly, and when she looked over at him and saw the pain in his face, she could stand it no longer.

"Johnny, it's all right, I understand."

"No, you don't, I hardly understand myself. I've loved you from the time we were kids and I used to chase after you and Angie, spoiling your tea parties and hiding your dolls. I used to watch you at school and then felt embarrassed because you were younger than me. When Tom began asking you out I hated myself for waiting all those years."

"We've known each other for such a long time . . . don't," she whispered, reaching up to touch his cheek.

"I have to, don't you see, the only way it will make sense to me is if I tell you. When I saw what Tom was doing I confronted him, asked him if he was going to try to make you happy. 'Sure, little brother,' he said, but I knew he was lying. One day we had it out. I told him you deserved better than him and he laughed and said that I wanted you for myself. I admitted I did. 'You'll never have her,' he said and turned to walk way."

He looked at her and she felt her heart reach out to him. She wanted to comfort him but she knew that he was determined to get the story out.

"I reached out to grab his shoulder but he turned around and swung at me. He missed but we both began swinging at each other and ended up in a fight. My parents heard us and came in and broke it up before it got out of control. Later, after you were married, when I saw what he was doing to you, I wanted to kill him. When he died I felt relief and guilt and shame. He was my own brother but I was glad he was not around to hurt you anymore."

"Oh, Johnny," Kit said, feeling tears slide slowly down her cheeks.

He put his arms around her. "Dont' cry, Kit, I won't be able to live with myself if I've hurt you, too."

She pulled back. "No, don't you see, we're like family you and me. We're brother and sister. It would have never worked out and one day we would have discovered that we were hurting each other because of it. Lisa is the one you love, Johnny."

"Honey, I do love you, but I love her so much that when I saw her in Adam's arms it tore my guts out."

"That's the way it's supposed to work, Johnny. The love we felt for each other is not the same thing."

"You knew and you agreed to marry me anyway."

This was going to be hard but she had to tell him the truth, he deserved that much.

"Johnny, you love this valley and this way of life and so do I. Adam is going to buy out my uncle and I thought if we were married it wouldn't be able to happen. I guess I knew deep down that it wasn't right."

He took her admission calmly then asked, "You and Adam, are you in love with him?"

"I don't know, I really don't. Anyway, he is playing the field like Tom did and I'm not about to experience that kind of relationship all over again."

"No, I don't think Adam is a bit like Tom. I've seen the way he looks at you and suspected all along that there might be something between you two."

"What is between us is Silverado. He wants it and is going to get it."

"Then let me help, please."

She shook her head. "I can't let you do that. You need to be with Lisa to plan your lives together."

"In a special way I'll always love you, Kit."

She smiled. "I know, me too. We should have left it at brother and sister." She slowly slipped the engagement ring off her finger and gave it to him. And then, suddenly, impulsively planted a kiss on his cheek.

He started the engine and turned the car back to the road for the drive to her house.

After that she found it was easy to tell her uncle something that he had guessed from the beginning. His reply was compassionate. "You did the right thing." He said no more on the subject.

At first the atmosphere in the retail shop was strained. Lisa darted out of her way, seeming unable to meet her gaze. But then Johnny came around after work to take Lisa home and Kit was able to laugh and tease them and Lisa relaxed.

She saw little of Adam as the summer days passed and fall fast approached. She didn't know if he were purposely avoiding her but she was glad for his absences because it gave her time to think about what she was going to do after the winery was sold. She would begin putting her portfolio together, with the hopes of finding a job in advertising. She would have to move away, of course, and that would be hard.

Meanwhile her uncle was given the medical okay to get married, so she filled the evening hours sitting in the kitchen with Willy planning their wedding. Willy had been a widow for many years and felt at first that she and Matt should slip away somewhere and get married without any fanfare. Kit pointed out that her family would feel cheated if they were not given the chance to share in their happiness.

Her Uncle Matt shrewdly left the two of them alone except to say that all he wanted was to marry Willy and that if she wanted all of the trimmings that would be fine with him. In the end it turned out that she did. She admitted it to Kit one evening.

"I've always thought I was too old to have a large wedding, honey. But you know, when I was young I ran away and got married. I've always regretted it."

"What about having a small wedding and a big reception?"

When she saw Willy's eyes light up she

knew she had hit on the perfect compromise. From then on it was easy. They arranged for a simple ceremony to take place in the church, for family members only, while all of their valley friends would be invited up to the house for the reception.

Adam continued to disappear for days at a time. Kit did not ask her uncle about his absences, assuming he had other business investments to handle and, besides, his comings and going were none of her business.

The day of the wedding finally arrived. It was a sunny morning in late August, warm with the thick smell of the grapes permeating the air. They were going to leave early to go to the church together and then return right after the ceremony in time to greet their guests arriving for the reception.

As Kit pulled her dress over her head she remembered how she felt on her wedding day, before quickly chiding herself for her foolishness. She would never allow herself to be married again. No, she would go to San Francisco to look for a job in advertising. She would become immersed in a career and forget men.

Her dress was a heather-colored silk with a modest neckline and a simple skirt that fell gracefully from her small waist into soft folds. She left her hair loose on her shoulders and in it she clipped a spray of baby's breath and tiny white roses.

She had argued with Willy that she had no place in the wedding party but Willy wouldn't hear of it. "You are like my own daughter. I've raised you since you were in pigtails, Kit, I want you and my granddaughter Ellie to stand up with me."

Adam was downstairs, waiting to drive them to the church. As she saw him her heart pounded with excitement. Tall and handsome, he was dressed in a dark blue suit with a snowy white shirt against his skin. He had acquired a tan since coming to the valley and now his darkened skin made a vivid contrast to the white dress shirt, accentuating his virile good looks. He glanced up as she stepped down the stairs.

She saw his eyes widen as he looked at her. They traveled down to her hand and skimmed her empty ring finger. Before the two of them could speak to each other her uncle came up behind her.

"Next to Willy this lady is the prettiest in the valley," he said giving her a kiss on the cheek.

Adam regarded them silently for a moment before answering in a low vibrant tone, "You are right about that, Matt."

The look in his eyes caused a giddy excitement to quicken her heartbeat. She smiled back, making a mock curtsy. When Willy came down the stairs all eyes turned to look up at her.

Her dress was a soft silver made of the lightest silk and she carried a bouquet of white roses tied with silver ribbons. Her face was beaming a smile at all of them. Kit looked over at her uncle and had to gulp back tears at the gentle loving look in his eyes.

"My dear, you look lovely," he said softly, for Willy alone.

She came up to him and the two exchanged a quick kiss in the small hallway. They looked up at Kit and Adam slightly embarrassed. Kit came to the rescue. "Hey, no kissing the bride before the wedding," she teased, lightening the moment.

There was general laughter all around as they turned to go out the front door.

She waited nervously at the back of the church. The signal was given and the small wedding party walked down the main aisle as the assembled relatives in the front turned their heads for their first view of the bride. She could feel Adam's eyes on her as she passed him, walking slowly, deliberately looking straight ahead at the altar.

She stopped as the minister took his place and the thoughts that she had tried to hold in check came flowing back, crowding out all others. Her own wedding had been a large one, with guests overflowing this same church. She had been giddy with excitement as Angie helped her into her white gown.

"Remember when we used to go to the

wedding shop in town and touch all of the gowns," Angie had whispered as Kit stood in front of the mirror, nervous and excited.

Then Tom had come in, despite Angie's admonition that it was bad luck to see the bride before the wedding.

"Sugar, you look good enough to eat," he had said, pulling her to him for a kiss.

She had melted at those words coming from her good-looking fiancé. She had always melted when he touched her, like the giddy schoolgirl she was.

Now, thinking back, she realized that Adam's touch moved her in a different way. With him there was a feeling of wanting to give as well as receive, of reacting as a woman instead of the self-centered child who had married Tom and thought only of her own needs.

She realized, now, that Tom's selfish immaturity matched by her own headstrong impulsiveness had made their marriage doomed from the start. Standing at the same altar where it had all begun for her and where it was beginning for Matt and Willy, she saw the difference that some added years and experience could make.

There were no last-minute qualms for either of them today. She knew they were mature adults who understood what was important in life and what was not. They had found each other after Matt nearly died and, after that discovery, came together naturally, comfortably and lovingly. That's the way it was supposed to be, she thought.

A quick glance over her shoulder confirmed that Adam's gaze was still riveted on her. She watched her uncle slip a plain gold band onto Willy's finger. Adam had a calm strength about him that Tom had never had. He took control of situations easily without having to bully people to his own point of view. Yet all along she had been comparing the two of them as if they were equals.

Maybe she was being unfair to him. She also wasn't giving her own feelings for him a chance. She was judging him on very little evidence and finding him guilty.

As the vows were repeated and a final blessing said over the newly married couple, Kit made a decision. She would put aside the past once and for all and face the future and Adam Redmont with a clean slate. She would try to trust again by listening to him without the shadow of Tom lurking in the background every time he spoke to her. She would judge him for what he was and not what she had expected him to be.

She blinked back tears as the ceremony ended and she joined her uncle and her new aunt as they walked down the aisle to the back of the church. Everyone was laughing and talking while they offered their congratulations to the newly wedded couple. She hugged them both before moving aside to let Willy's children and grandchildren move in to the crowded circle of well-wishers. As she did she felt a hand at her elbow and looked up to see Adam escorting her outside the church.

"Willy's daughter and her husband are going to bring them back up to the house. Why don't you ride back with me and we can start getting things ready for the reception?"

"Yes, that would be fine," she said, noticing how the gray eyes missed no detail of her heather-colored dress and the way it clung to her slender body.

The ride began in silence as he maneuvered his car into the traffic flowing back to the winery.

"Are you sorry?" he asked suddenly.

She looked at the firmly etched jaw and the way his hands clenched the steering wheel. Her answer was going to be an honest one.

"You mean about Johnny?" Seeing him nod curtly, she continued, "No, I'm not sorry. It was the right thing to do. I wouldn't have wanted to hurt Johnny or Lisa and I would have done both if we had gotten married. We've always been close, more like brother and sister than . . ." she hesitated.

"Lovers?" he asked.

"Yes."

He relaxed his grip on the wheel at her words. "What are you going to do now?"

"Oh, probably go to San Francisco to look for a job."

"Why don't you stay and work for me?"

"I don't know. . . ."

He considered her answer that wasn't really an answer for a moment before saying, "Let's talk about it later, okay, just keep an open mind on the subject."

Hadn't she promised herself she would do just that? "I will," she answered.

He glanced over at her, looking surprised at her reply. "Thank God," he said softly.

Kit stood off to the side, looking at her garden as the day slowly cooled off. Small round tables with shade-giving brightly colored umbrellas filled the garden and the driveway, and parked cars lined the road up Whistler Mountain. The reception had drawn people from all the families in the valley. Old-timers and their sons and daughters who had known Matt Carson for years had driven up in carloads to wish him and his new bride well and to rejoice over his recovery from his recent heart attack.

She looked over at her uncle now. He sat with his arm around Willy's shoulders, laughing and talking to two other older couples. He looked years younger at that moment, as his glance kept returning to Willy's face now wreathed in a happy smile. That's the way it should be, she thought. Love should make you happy, not miserable.

Out of the corner of her eye she saw Johnny and Lisa, sitting off to the side at a table by themselves, murmuring words for each other's ears alone. Angie and Ray were there. Her friend's pregnancy now beginning to show, tiny Angie made a perfect contrast to her husky protective husband. She had wisely kept her thoughts about Kit's broken engagement to her brother to herself, saying only, "Time heals, Kit, I think you are beginning to mend."

She sighed and turned to look at the garden. In the heat of the summer only the heartiest of the sun-loving plants had survived, but there was still a warm welcome feeling about the garden, despite the fact that it was not the riot of color it once had been. I do love it here, she thought, perhaps I should agree to work for Adam instead of moving away. It was only her pride getting in the way. Deep down she knew she would hate leaving this place. But how could she work for him? Everytime he looked at her, everytime he touched her, feelings of attraction and wanting surfaced. It was one thing to promise not to hate him but it was quite another to give in to the overpowering urge she had to be in his arms.

A hand on her shoulder made her turn around. She had been expecting it. He had taken off his jacket and tie and unbuttoned the first two buttons of his shirt. Dark hairs peeked out where his chest was exposed. She looked into the silvery eyes and found a gentleness that completely unnerved her.

"What are you doing off by yourself?" he asked in a quiet voice.

"Oh, just thinking."

"I think they'll be very happy together."

"I know that. That wasn't what I was thinking about."

Both hands were on her shoulders now, holding her lightly but their gentle pressure was making it very difficult for her. She wanted to throw herself into his arms and feel his body against hers.

"Oh?" he asked, tucking a finger under her chin and making her look at him. "What was it, then?"

"You, I was thinking about you," she blurted out for no reason except that the way he was looking at her made her feel that he knew anyway.

"What about me, Kitten?"

There it was again, the nickname that no one else ever called her but him. "I was wondering if I should accept your offer and work for you."

"That isn't something you have to decide today or tomorrow. The offer is there. I want you."

"To work for you, you mean."

He smiled, a slow easy smile that twinkled the silver highlights in the gray eyes like fragments of the shimmering sun. "That too."

Before she could answer she felt his lips brush her own in a light, feathery kiss.

"I want to ask you something, Kitten. I'm going to visit my brother for a few days and I'd like you to come with me."

"Your brother?"

"A real live older brother," he said, his broadening grin revealing white teeth. "He has a beach house on the coast north of here. I'd like you to come with me for the weekend. Don't worry, we won't be alone. Vince and Sally and their three children will be there."

She was tempted, very tempted. But even with his family there it would be dangerous to be alone with him. It would be difficult to keep a tight rein on her own wild urges.

"Don't say no," he whispered.

"I . . ." She wasn't going to say no.

"Matt and Willy need some time to be alone together. I've found someone to help Lisa in the store and to keep an eye on things while I'm gone."

"The harvest . . ."

He put a finger to her lips and silenced her. "The winery is completely ready for the harvest. Besides, I want to talk to you and this isn't the place to do it."

She stared up into the gray eyes which now seemed to hypnotize her with their intensity. She felt an overwhelming urge to be with him but more than that she wanted him to know that they were beginning again.

"I wasn't going to say no. I want to go with you."

He glanced over his shoulder at the crowded garden and then threw back his head and laughed a deep rumbling laugh. "You pick the damndest places to turn honest, my green-eyed Kitten. I'm not going to embarrass you right in the middle of this wedding reception, though I should for all of the torment you've put me through."

He drew an arm around her shoulders and turned her toward the party. Before they took more than a few steps, he whispered, "Don't forget to pack your bathing suit, the covered-up-crepe look is out at the beach."

As Angie looked over at them they were both convulsed with laughter.

Chapter Ten

$\mathcal{I}$ 've been wanting to get back down to the retail shop all summer and now I'm finally going to get my chance," Uncle Matt joked to Kit, as Adam carried her case to the car.

She knew he was telling the truth. Even after Willy made him promise not to spend more than a few hours in the shop, she knew he would enjoy pouring wine for the tourists while he gave them pointers on the places of interest in the valley. A glance over at Willy's conspiratorial wink confirmed that she knew it, too.

Adam was right, they needed time alone together. Still, that was not the only reason she was going and she knew it. She had given in to her feelings for him and pushed her doubts aside. Everyone at the wedding reception probably had been aware of the change, she reflected. After their encounter in the garden, they had spent the rest of the afternoon together holding hands while they laughed and visited with the guests.

"All set, Kitten?" Adam asked.

She nodded, climbed into the car and waved goodbye to her uncle and Willy. Then they made their way slowly down the hillside.

She looked over at Adam, who was dressed casually in tan slacks and an open-necked navy knit shirt. He caught her glance and smiled back.

"This weekend you can relax and enjoy yourself, Kitten."

She returned the smile, wondering if she would ever be able to relax again in his presence. All he had to do was look at her and her heart began beating faster.

They drove south for a short distance before turning west toward the coast. He seemed content to do the driving and not force her into conversation. She was just as glad to be able to calm her nervousness at the prospect of being alone with him for a weekend by enjoying the scenery of burgeoning grapevines lining both sides of the road, with lofty frost-reducing windmills standing like silent guardians of the grapes.

It was not long before they reached the rugged coast and turned onto the ribbon of highway that clung precariously to the jagged rocks that made up the northern California coastline. The tangy smell of the sea filled her nostrils when she rolled down the window to smell the delicious sea air.

Adam looked over lifting an eyebrow, "Smell as good as grapes?" he teased.

She laughed, "Well, almost as good. I've always liked this part of the coast. On a clear day like today you can see the fishing boats and the whitecaps and . . ."

She stopped as he reached for her hand and covered it with his own.

"Go on."

"Oh, well, you know," she finished lamely.

"No, I don't know but I want to get to know you, Kitten, and I want you to get to know me," his voice was oddly gentle.

"I'd like that," she admitted.

"Good," he said, squeezing her hand.

They drove in silence for a few minutes after that and Kit found herself relaxing her guard. Then he started telling her about his brother Vince, older by several years, his sister-in-law Sally and their three children.

She chuckled as he talked about the latest exploits of his nieces and nephews before turning and asking, "What about you? What have you been doing for the last twenty . . ." He looked at her quizzically.

"Twenty-six," she said, smiling.

"Twenty-six years. I want to know everything about you."

"Well, I was born very young," she began impishly.

"Ohhh," he groaned in mock pain, "I can see that this relationship is doomed."

She laughed again, this time a real laugh that reached all the way to her rib cage and shook her with laughter while all along the words "this relationship" kept repeating over and over in her brain. Then she stopped laughing and began telling him about Tom. She poured out feelings that had been bottled up for years. When she was finished he was quiet for a moment.

"I knew he had hurt you very badly but now I understand a lot of things I didn't before."

"Like what?"

"Like the fact that you are terrified of being hurt that way again. Well, you don't have to worry, sweet Kitten, I'll never hurt you."

If only I could believe him, she thought. She wanted to, wanted to forget the girl on the telephone and the one who had greeted him at the airport.

"Adam, I . . ."

"Shhh, don't say anything. I didn't intend for this conversation to go this far. Let's relax and enjoy the weekend."

The road twisted and turned as it snaked up the coast. Finally they turned off the highway onto a bumpy dirt road that led to a gravel driveway. They approached a large rambling beach house that stood on a gentle rise overlooking the sea. It was a one-story house made entirely of weather-roughened redwood and glass.

Several domed skylights interrupted its sloping roof, which slanted clear down to the front door, providing a slatted overhang that was a sheltered entranceway for the house. As they drew closer Kit's eyes were drawn to pots of vivid orange and yellow nasturtiums, which were grouped on a narrow wooden shelf that ran along the end of the house. Definitely a woman's touch, she thought.

They came to a stop and several small bodies came running toward them, with two black Labradors racing in front, barking their welcome.

"We're here," he laughed, grinning and braking to a stop.

The doors of the car were thrown open and two of the small bodies tried to crawl into his arms.

"Uncle Adam, Uncle Adam," they shrieked in delight.

"Give him a chance you two," a male voice called laughingly.

Kit stepped out of the car to see an older version of Adam, not as tall, but with the same gray eyes and curly black hair slightly graying at the temples. Next to him stood a petite blond-haired woman in her mid-thirties, wearing a casual denim skirt and a white sleeveless blouse. She smiled her welcome.

"You must be Kit, I'm Sally Redmont. I'm so glad you could come," she said.

One of the youngsters, who Kit discerned as

being around six years old, added, "She's as pretty as you said, Uncle Adam."

Kit looked up, surprised to find that he had discussed her with his family. He smiled, not at all embarrassed by the child's revelation. "She sure is, Teddy," he said, ruffling the boy's hair.

When they had sorted themselves out and Kit had been introduced to Vince, their cases were removed from the car and she was ushered into the house. As she stepped inside she drew a breath at what she saw. There were windows lining the whole side of the house that faced the sea. Low couches and chairs in off-white and beige tweed were scattered across the large living room, which encompassed the full length of the house, and a stone fireplace was tucked into one end of it. But it was the unobstructed view of the sea that caught her attention as she moved forward into the living room as if drawn by magnets to the swirling surf and beige mounds of sand piled up outside the windows.

"This is magnificent," she murmured.

"Thank you," Sally said, coming up behind her. "I love it here. The kids play on the beach all day and I can curl up and read or just walk along and think quiet thoughts."

"We hope you'll do whatever you like this weekend, Kit. There are no schedules of have-tos," Vince said.

She turned to look at him. Yes, she could see the family resemblance when he spoke. His face matched his brother's, with the same silvery-gray eyes and engaging grin that must be a Redmont trademark. But the extra years had mellowed the angles and planes of his face to a pleasing maturity, while Adam still had the rugged good looks of a young virile male.

"Let me show you to your room," Sally suggested, "then we'll have lunch."

She followed her down a hallway to a room that was also open to the sea, with sliding glass doors that provided her own private entrance. Rough California redwood made up the wall paneling, and the dresser was a light-colored teak, with matching teak night stands on either side of the bed. A fluffy beige comforter covered a modern bed, that was, to her surprise, a double bed.

Sally noticed her look at the bed and said, "One of the nice things about this wonderful house is that it can accommodate a lot of people. We decided to put double beds in all of the rooms, including the kids' rooms, to make it even more adaptable to company."

"It was good of you to have me," Kit said.

"I'm so glad you allowed Adam to bring you here. I've been wanting to meet you for a long time."

Kit wondered how long Sally had known about her but decided there was no polite way to ask.

"We're having sandwiches in the living room. Why don't you unpack and join us."

When she was left alone to put away the few clothes that she had brought with her she wondered what Adam had told his family about her. They all seemed to expect her and even to be eager for her arrival. So this was where he had been coming all summer during his absences from the winery. Now he had decided to share it with her. She reached her arms over her head in an excited stretch. This was going to be an eventful weekend, she was going to see the real Adam Redmont and she had a feeling that she would like what she saw.

During lunch Kit was introduced to Vince and Sally's children, Mike, the oldest, Teddy and an adorable little blond named Mandy. She learned that they lived across the bay from San Francisco, where Vince worked, and came to the beach house as much as possible during the summer. This was their last trip before school started. The children had been spending the summer in the sun and were tanned and healthy looking. They were dressed in their bathing suits and were eager to finish lunch and get back to the sand.

"What would you like to do this afternoon, Kitten?" Adam asked her as they helped Sally clear the coffee table in the living room where they had had their sandwiches.

"Take a sun bath, walk along the beach, look for shells . . ."

"Okay, okay, I get the picture," he grinned.

"Let's change into our bathing suits and meet outside."

She went back to the bedroom and closed the curtain, then slipped into her sea green bikini and pulled a thin, short, toweling robe of a matching color on over it. Putting some sun cream, her sunglasses and a towel and hat into a canvas carryall and sliding her feet into open-backed sandals, she pulled the curtain back, opened the sliding glass door and stepped outside.

The cool air ruffled her hair. The sea breeze blowing against her legs was refreshing after the valley heat.

"We're down here," came the cry from one of the youngsters as Kit looked out to see three small bodies busily making a sand castle on the beach.

"Hello, mermaid."

She spun around to find him standing beside her, wearing bathing trunks of a deep blue. His broad chest was covered by black curling hairs which tapered to a V at his waist. She could not recall whether she replied or not because the sheer male presence of him left her speechless.

He took her hand and led her down the narrow sloping sandy path to the beach below. Vince and Sally lounged on a large, flowered towel near the children and they turned and waved as they saw her and Adam approach.

But he kept on walking, leading her down the beach some distance from them. She set down her carryall and spread her towel down next to his. Then she untied the sash of her robe and dropped it on the beach.

When she looked over at him he was crouching down on his knees and his eyes were roaming her partially clad body with such thoroughness that she could feel the heat rising in her cheeks. She sat down on the towel and extracted a tube of sun cream from her carryall.

"Lie down and I'll rub this on your back," he said.

She lay on her stomach and felt the cool spurt of cream on the backs of her legs. He began rubbing the cream on her calves, and then on her thighs, with firm strokes. The feel of him touching her bare skin sent a shiver of excitement through her. Then his hand was at the small of her back with the rubbing becoming soft and caressing as he spread the cream on her back and shoulders.

In one brief movement the hook at the back of her bikini top was unfastened and he was caressing her bare back in long effortless strokes.

"Adam," she said, trying to tell him he must stop.

"Relax, Kitten, you'll get a better tan this way."

Even if she had wanted to protest further she was powerless against his hands, which slithered over her slick body causing a tingling awareness of their power with every long feather stroke. A rising excitement began in the pit of her stomach. She moaned softly. The sun cream forgotten, he slid his hands down her sides, touching the soft bulging breasts that were flattened against the towel.

Her heart pounded in her chest. She turned her head to the side and tried to tell him to stop but she could not make any sound come out of her mouth. Then abruptly the hands were withdrawn and her top quickly fastened.

"We've got company," he said, his voice thick with emotion.

"Uncle Adam, don't you and Kit want to help us build our castle?" a voice asked from behind her.

"It looks like you've already got it built, Teddy," Adam replied.

She sat up to look at the youngster who was standing in front of them, his big black dog at his side. The dog began licking her feet with its pink tongue, tickling her until she laughed and squirmed.

"Domino, stop," Adam said and the big dog sat quietly at the boy's side.

"Sorry folks," Vince said, coming up to stand beside his son. "Uncle Adam and Kit want to sunbathe, Teddy, let's you and I start another castle," he said to the youngster.

"Okay," was the amiable reply and the two of them and the big black dog moved off down the beach.

Adam looked over at her. "It's a good thing he stopped me, Kitten, because God knows I couldn't have stopped myself."

I couldn't have stopped you either, she admitted silently to herself, and I wouldn't have wanted to after a couple more minutes.

"I know," she said softly, unable to bring herself to admit the rest of what she already knew about her body's heightened response to his touch.

They sunbathed for a while before deciding to go walking along the beach. Adam took her hand as they walked over the wet sand, which gave way slightly with each step she took. She surmised that the beach was deserted on this sunny weekend because most of it was lined by high rocky cliffs with the sand accessible only by climbing down the sandy path which ran behind the Redmont beach house.

Kit looked back at one point to find that the others were mere specks on the horizon, so far had they come. Then she turned back, squinting at the sun and wishing she had brought her sunglasses. Adam stopped, then knelt down on the sand to look at something.

"What is it?" she asked, kneeling down beside him.

"Looks like a hermit crab. See the hole in the sand. As soon as we stopped the little fellow burrowed into the sand so we wouldn't spot him."

They were both crouching down, looking at

the tiny hole in the wet sand. When they straightened up, their eyes met. She saw a familiar glint in the gray eyes as he reached for her.

"I promised myself I would go slow this weekend but I can't keep my hands off you," he said low as he spread light feathery kisses across her face, her neck and her shoulders.

The effect on her was to ignite a fire that spread with lightning speed throughout her body and left her moaning softly.

"What did you say?" he asked, stopping the torrent of kisses with a ragged whisper.

"I . . . I don't want you to stop," she murmured, hungering for his touch.

He heard the words, then gently pushed her back into the sand, covering her body with his own. His tongue probed her lips until she parted them and felt it flicking gently inside her mouth. She responded by wrapping her arms around his neck and letting her fingers plunge into the curly black hair.

His kisses awoke an answering passion within her so that she pressed herself against him, her breasts crushed by the firm muscular chest and her body fevered with excitement by the hands which caressed the soft curves of her hips.

Deftly the bikini top was unhooked from the back and pushed aside. His hands cupped her breasts and she gasped in delight as his tongue teased and prodded her delicate nipples. Mindlessly she pressed herself closer to him, wanting to feel more of him against her soft skin.

His lips created a trail of fire across her breasts that spread to her rib cage and stomach as they plundered the sweetness of her silken skin. And then he was back on top of her crushing her to the sand and groaning her name into her ear.

It came up suddenly underneath him, icy cold water, spreading over their heated bodies. Kit yelped in surprise while Adam pulled back from her scowling fiercely. Together they stood up.

"Damn," he muttered, reaching down for her bikini top. "The tide is coming in." He handed her the top and the scowl turned into a sensual grin. "You were saved in the nick of time, Kitten. Luck must be on your side today. I don't seem to be able to exercise any self-control."

Self-consciously she fastened the top in place before looking into his face. Even with the sun glinting off his cheekbones the hunger was there. "I didn't want you to."

"Do you mean that?"

"I don't know what I mean anymore. When I'm with you I can't think straight."

"Then don't think at all," he said grabbing her by the shoulders as the water swirled around their ankles. "Just feel," he said as his lips came down on hers in a fierce kiss.

They slowly walked back to the beach

house. She marveled at the way she had totally lost herself to him. Her body had been aroused to the point where if he had wanted to take final possession of her she would have surrendered gladly. This was mad and crazy and perhaps she was the biggest fool on earth to let herself feel this way but she was not going to clamp down on her feelings, not anymore.

When they reached their towels, they realized the others had gone in. She gathered up her towel and carryall as Adam watched her, his hands brushing her legs to flick the sand off. As she straightened up he draped his arm around her shoulders and kissed her gently on the mouth.

"Hmmm, you're salty," she murmured.

"So are you," he whispered, kissing her again. "I'm crazy about salt."

"Hey, you two," a voice called out.

They looked up to see Vince, standing halfway down the sandy path that led to the house, waving at them.

"Okay," Adam waved back, "we're coming."

Turning to her he said, "There are too many people around here for my taste, five too many and two dogs. Let me help you carry this thing," he said as she giggled her response to the interruption. To pay her back he draped his other arm around her bare waist and hugged her to him as they walked up the path.

Vince grinned sheepishly as they approached. "The kids want a barbecue on the beach tonight. I thought you might like to relax before we light up the fire."

"Sounds great," Kit replied. "I think I'll shower off some of this sand."

She walked toward her bedroom door and heard Adam mutter, "Great timing, big brother."

The shower spray hit her body with delicious warmth, washing the grainy sand from her skin. She found herself singing a dreamy romantic song. She had never sung in the shower before, but then, she had never responded to any man the way she responded to Adam. Not even Tom. With him it had been as if she were a child that he was coaxing to womanhood. Sometimes she had balked at the things he wanted to do. But with Adam it felt so right. She was no longer an impulsive child, she was a woman with womanly needs and she knew instinctively that he would be able to satisfy them as no man had ever done.

With every fiber of her being, she had wanted him as they lay in the sand. She had thrown caution to the winds and had told him so, too. Whatever happened now, she knew that, given another chance, she would respond in the same way.

She stepped out of the shower and reached for a large towel to wrap around her. Then she opened the bathroom door and stepped into her bedroom. She decided on blue jeans and a soft mint green V-necked velour top with long sleeves to wear for the barbecue. She brushed her hair until it lay soft and loose on her shoulders.

There was a knock at the door.

"Come in," she called.

The door opened to admit the Redmont's young daughter, Mandy. "Hi," she said, her smile revealing two missing teeth.

"Hi, sweetie," Kit said, kneeling down in front of her.

"Mom sent me to see if you were ready," she said, lisping slightly because of the missing teeth.

"As a matter of fact I am," Kit said, straightening up and slipping her hand into the small hand. "I'll need you to show me where to go though."

"Sure," Mandy said as she led her from the bedroom, down the hallway, through the living room, into a very homey kitchen at the other end of the house. Sally was standing at the counter slicing vegetables as they entered.

"Oh, Kit," she said looking up, "I didn't mean for Mandy to bring you here. I thought you'd like to go back down to the beach where they're lighting the fire."

"Let me help you, please," Kit said walking toward the counter.

"That would be great. We don't stand on ceremony here. If a guest offers to help, I'll take her up on it," Sally laughed, handing her a slicing knife.

185

Mandy wandered off and the two were left alone in the kitchen.

"I understand you're from the Napa Valley," Sally said, taking some hamburger patties from the refrigerator.

"Yes, my Uncle Matt took me in to live with him when I was very young and I've spent my whole life in the valley." Before she knew it she was telling Sally about the winery and her uncle and how he built it up over the years. They worked together preparing the food for the barbecue and the words seemed to flow out of her as she chopped vegetables for the salad and mixed them in a large plastic container.

"Your uncle sounds like a wonderful man," Sally said when she had finished.

"He's the only family I have, he and my new Aunt Willy, that is."

"You know Adam has been coming here off and on all summer and we began hearing about you from him. I'm so glad he found you, Kit, he's needed someone like you for a long time."

Kit looked up from the picnic hamper, not knowing quite how to respond.

Sally caught her look and said quickly, "Forgive me, I didn't mean to embarrass you. It's just that, next to Vince, Adam is one of my favorite people in the whole world. I know that traveling all over the country was interesting and fun for him for a while but lately he's seemed to have grown discontented with that kind of life, as Vince did many years ago. I could see him wanting to settle down and stay in one place. Maybe now he's found the kind of life he wants."

"He's been very kind to my uncle, especially during his heart attack," Kit replied, feeling foolish because she was at a loss for words. Adam had been honest from the beginning, she realized that now, and Sally had confirmed it.

"Oh, Adam is kind and in many ways unselfish, even though there have been many . . ."

"Daddy sez he's coming to help you with the food," Mandy said from the doorway.

Sally stopped after the interruption and quickly finished packing the hamper. Kit wished she had finished her sentence. Had she been going to say many women? If only Mandy had waited two more seconds before making her announcement.

Vince entered and took all the provisions for the day, then led them away to the beach. Kit followed to a place where a fire pit was lit and coals glowed red hot. Wood was piled up nearby for a real fire after the barbecue.

From a distance she could see Adam throwing a football to his two nephews, who were running across the stretch of beach. He also wore blue jeans and an old T-shirt. His face had a happy smile as he signalled for Mike to go wide for a pass. As she stood looking at him she found herself thinking about the kind of father he would make with his own sons. He turned, saw her and waved and she was instantly embarrassed at where her thoughts had taken her as she waved back. He probably knew she had been watching him, but did he also know what she had been thinking?

The barbecue was a big success, judging from the number of hamburgers that were eaten. Adam sat next to her on the blanket that had been spread out in front of the fire pit. He laughed and joked with his brother and she was touched at the boyish change his face underwent when he was with his family.

After the coals had burned down, the wood was added to the pit and a warm toasty fire crackled on the darkening beach. They took long sticks and put marshmallows on the end to toast in the fire. The night turned cool as the sun went down. Kit shivered slightly and moved closer to the comforting warmth of his body. Someone started to sing and before long they all joined in singing the familiar words of an old campfire song.

As she sat next to him, his deep voice ringing out next to her filling the night air, she was filled with a deep contentment that she had not felt for many years. The stars came out, and they continued singing one song after another. Finally Vince and Sally gathered up their children and the empty food hamper and began to head back up to the house.

"No need to rush in," Vince said, "It's a great night but the flock needs to get to bed."

Mandy was asleep in his arms as he turned to lead the others to the house.

"We'll be up in a little while," Adam drawled behind him.

The other youngsters said good night, then flicked on their flashlights so that they could find their way up the path to the house. Kit watched the bobbing circles of light bouncing over the dark beach until they disappeared and a light went on in the house at the top of the path.

The crackling fire was the only sound filling the quiet beach. She sat in the circle of Adam's arms, hoping he would resume his earlier lovemaking but he was strangely quiet. She leaned her head back on his shoulder and watched the firelight illuminate his face.

"What are you thinking?" she asked softly.

He looked down at her and brushed a light kiss across her forehead. "This is the first time we have been alone together with no interruptions since we arrived. I am enjoying it."

A heady feeling of happiness swept through her at his words. "I am too," she responded.

Slowly his other arm came around her and his lips came down on hers. The kiss was gentle, filled with none of the passion of the afternoon. She wondered briefly if she had done something to displease him. She looked up questioningly as he pulled his lips back. He knew what she was thinking.

"Kitten, all I've done since we've met is rush you. I don't want to do that now," he said, kissing her eyelids.

His voice had an intensity about it that she had not heard before, telling her that this was the truth. Unable to resist the irony of the situation she giggled.

"What's that for?" he asked, kissing the tip of her nose.

Her heart thudded in her chest and a wild excitement overtook her. He must want her very much and he must care for her very much to hold himself in control waiting for her to take the lead. She knew that she could resist him no longer.

"You've decided to go slow but I don't want you to," she said a little breathlessly.

"Oh, honey," he groaned.

The lips that came down on hers were no longer gentle and no longer controlled but rather they were filled with a passion that raged across her own body like a roaring inferno. She responded recklessly, her restraint gone, her doubts pushed aside. She wrapped her arms around his neck and pressed herself against him.

He leaned her back onto the blanket and she lost herself in his deep drugging kisses. He was murmuring low unintelligible words in her ear while her body was soaring like a rocket with the feel of him against her. His hands caressed her spine and her rounded hips and his lips left a trail of fire down her neck, ending at the dusky hollow between her breasts.

"I want you, Kitten," he said in a low husky voice, "I want to make love to you."

"Yes, yes," she gasped out weakly, overcome by her own fierce emotional response to him.

"Not here, not now," he said, pulling her gently to a sitting position. "I want to savor every inch of you and I want you to enjoy it as much as I will. This beach is too cold and," he glanced up at the lighted house, "not too private. The family will be leaving tomorrow afternoon, say you'll stay here until Monday with me and we can have the house to ourselves."

Her nerves were reeling with the assault on her senses of his ardent lovemaking. It was no use, she would be foolish to pretend otherwise.

"I'll stay," she said in a shaky voice.

He smiled broadly and nuzzled her ear. "The next twenty-four hours are going to be the longest of my life," he whispered. "And now, my Kitten, we'd better go in before I forget everything I've just said and make love to you on this cold, not very private blanket."

He helped her to her feet and together they folded the blanket and put out the fire. Then he turned and kissed her once more, feverishly, hungrily. "This is going to have to last me for a long time," he said.

Chapter Eleven

It was not until the sun's rays penetrated the bedroom curtains, casting its warm glow throughout the room, that she blinked her eyes open. Kit felt as if she had been drugged as she stretched her arms overhead and yawned in an effort to wake up. She hadn't slept that soundly in years. She looked at the clock on her night stand and was surprised to find that it was already after nine o'clock. There was a soft knock at her door.

"Come in," she called in a sleepy voice.

The door opened and Sally came in carrying a glass of orange juice.

"I hope I didn't wake you up," she said. "All the others have already gone down to the beach except for Teddy and so I thought I'd bring you some juice."

"No, I just woke up. I can't believe it's so late," Kit said reaching out and taking the juice that was handed to her. "Hmmm, thank you, this is good," she said as she set it on the night stand. "What's wrong with Teddy?"

"I don't know. Last night before he went to bed he didn't feel good. Now he says his stomach hurts, and he feels like he's got a temperature. It could be too many hamburgers or he could be coming down with something. I'm going to watch him for a few hours and see. We may have to leave early if he is really sick."

"Is there anything I can do to help?"

"Not a thing," Sally said, smiling. "Oh, yes, you might want to go down to the beach and keep Adam company, he's been prowling around here like a bear all morning waiting for you to wake up. I finally had to shoo him out."

Kit smiled and leaned back against the pillows. "That will be a pleasure," she laughed.

"I'm so glad, Kit," Sally said, beaming a smile at her. "I'm going to check on Teddy, breakfast is warming in the kitchen, help yourself."

When she left, Kit bounded out of bed.

As she made her way down to the beach she saw Mike and Mandy flinging sticks across the sand for their two dogs to fetch while Adam and Vince sat back on a towel watching them. The two brothers appeared to be deep in conversation as she approached. Adam turned his head just as she reached them, a smile lighting up his face. Vince too turned around, waved, then diplomatically sauntered over to his two children.

Adam, wearing blue jeans and a knit pullover shirt, came up beside her. He looked happy and relaxed. "Don't I get a good morning kiss?" he asked, taking her carryall and setting it in the sand.

She leaned over and gently touched his cheeks with her lips.

"I'd hardly call that a kiss, Kitten, but never mind, we'll remedy that later."

She knew from the heat rising in her cheeks that she was blushing. She was feeling less brazen in the cool light of morning than she had under the stars but she was not going to change her mind now.

"Not a thing in the world to be embarrassed about, sweet, we're going to enjoy it." He grinned a wolfish grin as he let his gaze drift down to her bikini-clad body, which was partially covered by the toweling robe. "My God, but we're going to enjoy it."

She laughed in spite of herself as he took her arm and led her to the towel. This time they stayed with the others, laughing and joking with Vince and throwing sticks for the two black Labradors to fetch. At one point Mandy came up to her, put her small hand in hers and led her over to see a pile of shells that she had collected.

After exclaiming over the collection Kit returned to Adam's side and noticed that Vince was no longer with them.

"He's gone up to the house to check on Teddy," he said. "He's worried about the little guy."

They proceeded to play with the other two youngsters until it was time for lunch. Then all four of them decided to go back up to the house. Mandy held Kit's hand as they trooped up the path and pulled open the sliding glass doors to the living room.

"Hey, where is everybody?" Mike called into the house.

"Let's try Teddy's bedroom," Adam said.

They found Sally sitting on the edge of the young child's bed, holding his hand, and Vince on the phone in the hall. The other two youngsters, sensing that something was wrong, entered the room very quietly.

Sally looked up from the bed. "I'm so glad you're back," she said to the assembled group, attempting to sound calm. "Teddy is very sick and we may have to take him to the hospital."

"We think he may have appendicitis," Vince said in a low voice, coming to stand next to them. "He has a high fever and has been complaining that the pain in his stomach has moved to his side."

Kit looked over at the little boy lying in the big double bed and felt her heart go out to him. His face was pale and he whimpered softly to his mother.

"What are you going to do?" Adam asked.

"I just phoned the emergency room at the hospital and they say to bring him right in."

"Then both of you go now. Kit and I will watch Mike and Mandy."

"You're sure?" Vince asked looking over at Kit.

"Please go now. I'd be glad to stay here with the others," Kit said.

After that the room seemed to explode into activity. Vince picked up his son, bedclothes and all, and carried him outside to the car. Sally quickly followed, giving Adam and Kit last minute instructions about where the food was and telling the others to mind Uncle Adam and Kit. She agreed with Adam that she should go with Vince because the drive to the hospital would be a long one from their isolated beach house and she felt Teddy would need comforting and watching, she told Kit.

"Everything here will be fine," Kit reassured her as she hurried out the door.

"Uncle Adam, is Teddy gonna be all right?" Mandy asked fearfully after they had left.

"Of course he will, honey," he said, picking up the little child and kissing her on the forehead.

But as Kit looked over at him she saw the worried frown on his face.

"Let's have some lunch," she said, trying to sound cheerful and relax the two children.

The afternoon seemed to crawl by after lunch. They decided not to go down to the beach lest Vince call and they miss hearing the telephone ring. They changed back into slacks and then the children played games on the living room floor.

They had brought all kinds of puzzles and board games from home and as the afternoon slowly slipped away they settled down in front of the big glass window to play with them. Adam tried to lighten the mood by joking with them and both he and Kit crouched on the floor to join in their games. But despite their efforts an uneasy tenseness hung in the air, for the missing child was on everyone's mind.

As the sun set in the sky Kit wandered into the kitchen and looked inside the refrigerator for something to make for dinner. She heard the telephone ring and quickly went back to the living room. Adam was on the phone talking in low tones while the two youngsters stood beside him. It was impossible to guess what was going on because of all the noise Mike and Mandy were making with their questions.

Then he put the phone down. "Teddy is going to be okay, everybody," he said, picking Mandy up in his arms.

"What happened?" Kit asked from the doorway.

"He had to have his appendix removed, but it was caught in time and there is no danger. Vince and Sally are going to spend the night in town, then Vince will be out here in the morning."

"Uncle Adam, what's appendix?" Mandy asked.

"Aw, everybody knows what that is," Mike said.

"Honey, it's a part of your body that you used to need a long time ago but you really don't use anymore. Sometimes it has to be removed," Adam replied, looking over at Kit.

"Let's everybody try to guess where your appendix is located?" she suggested.

And with that the atmosphere in the room lightened as the children made various guesses where their appendix might be found and Kit and Adam laughed uproariously with them as each guess became more outrageous than the next.

Dinner was a loud boisterous affair in the homey kitchen. Kit suggested that each person prepare something for dinner to give the children something to do and so all four of them jostled and bumped into each other as they made trips back and forth to the refrigerator for their specialties. Mandy made peanut butter and jelly sandwiches, Mike concocted chocolate sodas, Kit added a green salad and Adam turned a couple of canned goods they had found into creamed tuna on toast that was delicious.

"I didn't know you could cook," Kit said to him as they were setting the food on the table.

"There's a lot about me you don't know," he said softly. She looked up to find he was watching her. "And there's a lot more you're going to find out," he added.

She could say nothing in return except to smile. She had forgotten what they had agreed to last night, after worrying about Teddy all day. Was that what he was referring to or did he mean something more permanent? Deep down she was wishing it was the latter but the serious gray eyes held no clue.

The dinner was a huge success. Each person presented his or her dish while the others raved about how delicious it was. Only Mike started to break the mood when Mandy set down her peanut butter sandwiches.

"No one eats peanut butter for dinner, dopey," he said.

Adam looked over at him, picked up one of the sandwiches and took a bite out of it. "I do," he said deliberately.

Mike, sensing his uncle's displeasure, said, "Well, I guess it will be okay."

After eating and cleaning up the kitchen the four of them went into the living room and Adam began to tell stories. Not only had he traveled all over the United States, but he had been in many foreign countries, and entertained them for several hours with tales of interesting places he had seen and people he had met. Mandy listened, sitting snugly in Kit's lap, but Kit sensed that the youngster was still worried about her brother and upset by the absence of her parents.

When bedtime was announced she clutched Kit's hand in a tight grip.

"Are you sure Teddy is okay?" she asked.

"Of course he is," Kit said, kissing her lightly on the forehead.

Kit looked over at Adam and seeing his raised eyebrows knew he had not heard the remark. Before she realized what she was saying, she blurted out, "Come and sleep with me tonight, honey."

Adam heard that offer she knew by the rueful smile that appeared on Adam's face and the way he dug his fingers through his curly hair.

"You're very lucky to have Kit here, Mandy, you know that?" he asked the youngster.

She saw a strange light in the silvery eyes that told her he understood what she had done but there was something else there, too, for a moment, that puzzled her.

"Mike are you going to be all right alone in your room?" Adam asked.

"Course, Uncle Adam. I'm not a baby."

"No, sport, you're not," he replied picking up Mandy. "I'll carry her to your bedroom," he said to Kit.

She followed him down the hallway, opening the bedroom door for him. He walked in with Mandy in his arms and set her on the bed. "Go to sleep little one, Teddy is going to be fine," he said, kissing her forehead.

"Isn't Kit coming to bed now?" the youngster asked.

"Yes, I suppose she is," Adam said dryly. "But I'd better kiss her good night, too, don't you think?" he asked, smiling a wicked smile.

Mandy looked up at the two of them, "Sure."

He held Kit's face in his hands, kissing her gently and very briefly. After not being near him all day she almost groaned her disappointment out loud when he released her. He knew what she was thinking and whispered, "Sorry," as he let her go.

The gray eyes twinkled with amusement. He was not sorry at all. He had done it on purpose to tease her. Even so, she could not suppress a giggle as she shut the bedroom door.

The delicious aroma of frying bacon wafted from the kitchen as Kit and Mandy walked in the next morning, hungry for breakfast. They found Mike already seated at the table and Adam at the stove.

"Good morning," he smiled at the two of them. "Sleep well?" he asked innocently, with the same amused glint in his eyes.

"Very well," Kit smirked back then began to laugh at the unspoken joke between them.

"Bet you're surprised that Uncle Adam can cook all kinds of things," Mike said, misinterpreting her laughter.

"Very surprised," Kit replied softly, watching as Adam dished up generous portions of bacon and eggs for the four of them.

In truth she was not thinking about his cooking ability but about how easily they managed with the two children. It was almost as if the children were their own and they were an old married couple sitting down to breakfast together. All weekend in fact had gone smoothly except for Teddy's illness. The Redmonts accepted her as one of the family and she in turn felt happy and relaxed in their company. She knew she was rushing things but, all of a sudden, being with Adam seemed so right that she couldn't stop herself.

"Vince called earlier to say that Teddy is doing fine and he will be here sometime this morning to pick up some of his things."

"Is he in the hospital?" Mandy asked.

"He is in the hospital until he recovers from the surgery and then he will come home, honey," Adam replied.

"Do we have to go home today?" Mike asked, sounding disappointed.

"Let's wait until your dad gets here, sport," Adam answered, giving Mike an encouraging smile.

Kit wished they would be able to stay at the beach house a little longer. She was seeing a different side of Adam now and she liked what she saw. She liked it very much.

"Mmmm, delicious," she said taking a sip of his freshly brewed coffee. "My compliments to the chef," she smiled as she spoke.

"Thank you, Ma'am," he grinned back and the two children giggled at this silly display between grown-ups.

Mike and Mandy quickly finished their

breakfast and went to gather up their beach toys while Kit helped Adam do the breakfast dishes. After they left Kit decided to bring up the subject of last night.

"I hope it was all right for Mandy to sleep with me. She looked so frightened and scared that I couldn't resist."

"I think it was nice of you, Kit. There'll be other nights for us," he said in a low voice that made her shiver with excitement. "Let's change into our swim suits, at least I can look at that delicious body of yours at a distance," he added.

They heard a car door slam and hurried to the front door expecting to see Vince. Emerging from a low-slung red sports car was the girl Kit had seen at the airport. There was no mistaking her dark hair and the smile of pleasure on her face at seeing Adam. She wore tight-fitting designer jeans and a blouse knotted at the midriff which revealed her ample curves.

"Adam," she said, throwing herself into his arms.

"Caroline," he muttered.

So this was Caroline, the girl who had met him at the airport and had telephoned him at her home. Kit suddenly felt as if this meeting was inevitable. Maybe the weekend had been too good to be true from the time she arrived.

"Kit, this is Caroline Sinclair. Caroline, Kit Carson," Adam said, detaching Caroline's arms from around his neck.

The other woman's eyes narrowed for a fraction of a second before she burst into a throaty laugh. "Surely this is some kind of a joke?" she asked.

"It's not a joke," Kit replied evenly, choosing to interpret her remark as referring only to her name. "My name is really Katherine but I've been called Kit ever since I was a child."

Caroline paid no attention to the explanation. She turned back toward Adam, linking her arm possessively through his.

"When you called last night and told me what had happened I knew that I had to come," she said to him. "I've known Teddy since he was born," she added for Kit's benefit.

Kit could feel herself growing tense as she looked at the two of them. So, he had called her last night to tell her the news about Teddy while all the time Kit had thought he was lying in his cold bed thinking of her. Now, standing there, she noticed he made no effort to disengage his arm. Caroline began talking to him in low whispering tones, for his ears alone. She could stand it no longer.

"Excuse me, I'd better check on Mike and Mandy," she said, turning back to the house.

Her stomach was in a tight knot as she walked down the sandy path to the beach. Had she been right all along? Had he been using her? She had almost given in to him and to herself, she thought, brushing tears from her eyes.

Mike and Mandy were busy building sand castles and appeared to be content for the moment. She sat down in the warm sand and looked out at the sea. It was a gray green, with a brisk wind whipping the whitecaps to a frothy foam. Inside, her stomach was churning as well. She had begun to trust Adam during this weekend and to think he cared for her. Now, after seeing him with Caroline, she feared that she had been a fool. She blinked away hot tears as she recalled the intimate look Caroline had given him. He had never explained what had happened that day at the airport, she recalled, thinking back, except to blame her for running out.

Was she never going to learn? Was her whole life going to be filled with handsome men who deceived her? Everyone told her Adam was different and she had made herself believe it. Oh, Adam, she prayed silently, please don't turn out like Tom. She heard them coming from the house but could not make herself move from her place on the sand.

"Mike and Mandy, how are you, darlings?" she heard Caroline ask.

The youngsters looked up and gave her a desultory "Hi" before going back to their sand castle.

Adam spread a blanket out for Caroline.

"Poor, poor Teddie," she said, turning to Kit. "I think it is really sweet of you to help Adam look after Vince's children, Miss Carson."

Kit could tell by the harsh look in her eyes that she didn't think anything of the kind.

"It was nice of Vince and Sally to have me for a weekend guest, it's the least I could do," she replied.

"Uncle Adam," Mandy called, "make Mike stop throwing sand at me."

Adam stood up and walked over to where the two youngsters had stopped playing and were now fighting.

"You know," Caroline said, leaning over to Kit, "when Adam asked me to come up here this weekend I had to say no because of a previous appointment I simply couldn't break. But after he called me and I heard what had happened to poor Teddy I simply had to drop what I was doing and rush up here to help."

"How kind of you," Kit said dryly. She didn't know whether to believe her or not. Had Adam asked her here for the weekend only after he learned that Caroline wouldn't be able to come?

He was now back, holding a tearful Mandy by the hand.

"I wasn't throwing sand. He started it. I've got some in my eye."

"Let me take you to the house and help you wash it out," Kit said, willing to do anything to separate herself from Adam and his companion and at the same time feeling sorry for poor Mandy. The youngster was obviously still worried about Teddy and having a difficult day as a result.

Adam released Mandy and the child ran over to Kit. She looked up and caught the silvery gray eyes probing hers. She glared back at him, saying nothing, before gathering Mandy up and leading her back to the house.

A quick examination revealed that Mandy did have sand in her eyes, so Kit led her to the bathroom to wash it out with handfuls of cold water. Mandy cried while the grains of sand were rinsed from her eyes but quickly recovered. When the cold bath was over, she put her arms trustingly around Kit as she dried her face with a fluffy towel.

"Don't like Caroline," she whispered in her ear.

Kit looked at her. "Of course you do."

"No," Mandy insisted. "She's mean."

"Honey, that's not a nice thing to say about someone."

"Don't care. She comes up here all the time and tries to spoil things."

Kit could not think of anything to say or do except to give Mandy a reassuring hug before leading her back to the beach. So, Caroline was at the beach house all of the time. It was probably just as she had said, this weekend she wasn't able to come and Adam asked Kit as a replacement.

As they approached the others Kit saw that Caroline had found time to slip a bathing suit under her outfit before she "rushed up here" and had now removed her jeans and blouse to reveal a bikini that allowed a generous glimpse of her full breasts and curving hips.

When she saw Adam smoothing suntan lotion on her back, she felt a stab of pure rage as she recalled how that intimate act was performed on her only yesterday. It was his soft caresses that had made her admit how much she wanted him, now he was caressing Caroline with every bit of intensity that he had shown to her.

"Hmmm, delicious," Caroline purred.

Mandy walked back over to Mike and his sand castle as Adam looked up at Kit.

"Aren't you going to put your suit on today?" he asked.

"No, I got overexposed yesterday, I'm going to cover up today so I won't get burned."

His eyes narrowed slightly at her choice of words. Even though they were said nonchalantly, he knew what she meant. He finished with Caroline's back, then she sat up to kiss him on the cheek.

"Thank you, sir," she said sweetly, leaning over so that he had an excellent view of her voluptuous figure.

In another moment, Kit thought, she would pick up a handful of sand herself and throw it at the two of them.

"Daddy," Mandy yelled and they all turned around to see Vince striding down the sandy path.

The children stopped their play and ran over to him. He picked up Mandy in his arms and, with Mike trailing beside him, came over to the others. Kit and Adam stood up, Caroline continued lounging indolently in the sun.

"How is he?" Adam asked.

"He's going to be fine. When I left he was still asleep. Sally wanted to be there when he woke up."

"Do we have to go home, Daddy?" Mike asked.

Vince looked at Kit and Adam and for the first time appeared to notice Caroline on the nearby blanket.

"We intended to leave today, now, I don't know," he said.

"Let me stay here and close up the house for you, Vince dear," Caroline said, standing up at last and sauntering over. "I've spent enough time here that I can do it easily."

"Caroline, how did . . . ?"

"Adam called me last night and told me about Teddy. I don't mind helping out here, honestly," she said.

"We don't want to go home," chorused Mike and Mandy.

Vince released the two of them. "I came back to gather up some of Teddy's things and take them back to the hospital. Your mother's going to need some fresh clothing, too. We haven't decided what to do about you two poppets."

"I'll stay here as long as you want me to, or I

can take the kids back to your house," Adam said quietly to his brother.

"If you don't mind I'd like to keep the kids here for today and then check back tomorrow after I see how Teddy is doing."

Kit made up her mind quickly. She did not want to stay here with Adam and Caroline one minute longer than necessary. The other woman obviously was not going to leave. Well, she wanted Adam, she was welcome to him.

"I'd like to go back with you, Vince. I really hadn't planned on being gone more than two days. I can drive back to the hospital with you and then call someone to pick me up."

She purposely avoided looking at anyone but Vince when she spoke. There was a moment of silence before Mandy said, "I don't want Auntie Kit to go."

Only Adam said nothing. When her eyes met his she could see that he was angry. He looked at her hard and long, before he turned away to talk to Vince.

"Thank you for coming, Miss Carson," Caroline said, dismissing her as if she were a servant. "I can take over now."

"My pleasure," Kit shot back, "I'm sure you can." She turned to go back to the house to pack her things.

She was in the bedroom putting her clothes together when she heard footsteps approach. She turned and saw him enter the room and close the door.

"Coward," he said in a low angry voice.

"I don't know what you are talking about," she said, turning back to the bed where her clothes were laid out.

His arm was on her shoulders spinning her around. "You are a coward, Kit Carson. Do you think that by running away from here you are going to run away from your own feelings?" he asked angrily.

"I don't feel anything for you, not a thing," she lied.

"Yesterday you felt something for me," he said, his anger simmering to a rage. "You wanted me and I could have taken you on the beach if I'd wanted to."

"That was before your girlfriend arrived," she said, hating the jealousy and anger in her voice.

"My girlfriend?" he threw back his head and laughed.

This was too much for Kit. She swung her arm up and hit his face with a resounding slap. He grabbed her wrists and imprisoned her arms behind her back.

"Listen to me, you little wildcat. I had no idea Caroline was coming up here and your behaving like this isn't going to help the situation at all."

"Let go of me," she yelled, trying to twist out of his grasp. "You telephoned her didn't you?"

"Yes, I did but . . ."

That was enough for her. She gave him a vicious kick in the shins. With a grunt of pain he released her.

"She called you at my house and you called her last night, how cozy," she raged, her green eyes burning in anger.

"So it was you on the other phone," he said. "I don't have time to explain things to you now but I want to tell you that whatever you're thinking in that mixed-up head of yours is wrong. I'm not Tom."

"You may not be but you could pass for him now," she said, not caring how loud her voice was.

"Doesn't trust mean anything to you? After all that's happened between us couldn't you trust me long enough for me to explain?"

"I don't want to hear your explanation and there is nothing between us but the winery. You want it and you'll do anything to get it, even romancing the owner's niece."

Kit had never seen him so furious. His eyes were like flinty steel, his mouth pulled into a tight angry line and a muscle twitched along the side of his jaw. She knew if she had been a man he would have struck her.

Instead he spoke calmly, almost matter-of-factly, "You are going to have a sad unhappy life if you don't trust anyone or believe in anyone. I pity you."

When he said that, she felt something snap inside of her and she began shaking. Tom had said the same thing when she had confronted him with her knowledge of his girlfriend. Well, no one, not Tom, not Adam, not anyone was going to pity her ever again.

"I hate you. I don't want you to touch me again. I don't want to see you again. You can buy the winery but you can't buy me," she screamed at him.

"My God, get a grip on yourself, you're getting hysterical," he said reaching out to touch her.

"No," she shrieked. "This time the great lover strikes out. How many women do you have to have before your massive male ego is satisfied? Go back to Caroline, you deserve each other. Stay out of my life!"

"Look at yourself," he said, "Take a good hard look at yourself. Can no one reach you?"

"Get out of here," she screamed, throwing clothes at him. "Get out, get out."

"Goodbye, Kitten," he said and left the room, slamming the door behind him.

I will not cry, she told herself. I will not ever cry again for all of the deceitful men in this world. I'm strong and I will get over this one, too.

The drive back to the valley was a quiet one. She did not doubt that Vince had heard her argument with Adam but he chose to leave her to her own thoughts rather than probe into what had happened.

As she sat in the car watching the scenery sweep past, she stopped blaming herself for being a fool and started thinking about what she would do now. She could begin looking for a job immediately, now that things between her and Adam were finished. She had an old college friend who lived in San Francisco and she could call her as soon as she got back and ask to stay with her while she went job hunting. She hated to leave the winery but it would be impossible to stay now.

Kit went with Vince to visit Teddy at the hospital. She knew that Sally was surprised at her appearance there but she also chose to say nothing, instead she hugged her and reassured her that Teddy was going to be fine. The little fellow was pale as he lay in his hospital bed but his natural good spirits came through despite his weakened physical condition.

Vince would not hear of her calling someone to pick her up but insisted that he drive her home. As they turned up Whistler Mountain she heard him say softly, "He always wanted a place like this."

Assuming that he was talking about Adam, she said nothing. Well, he's going to have his winery, she thought. After all, he deserved it, he worked hard for it. He took her out, pretended to care for her, almost seduced her, all in the name of business. If she thought for one moment that her uncle would put up a fight, she would have done anything to stop Adam from getting control of Silverado, but one look at her uncle and Willy as they met her at the door and she knew for sure that they had already decided that what they had between them was far more important than anything else.

The explanations she feared she would have to make to her uncle were never made. After Vince left he started to question her but Willy shook her head ever so slightly and he stopped. She was able to get to her room before the tears that she had kept bottled up all afternoon spilled out.

She flung herself on her bed, crying and sobbing as if her heart would break. Her pillow was drenched by the flood of tears she shed. After the storm passed she was exhausted. She didn't even have any anger left in her, only an aching numbness filled every inch of her body.

She splashed cold water on her swollen red eyes and looked at herself in the mirror. She would not be beaten, she would call Sandy tomorrow. There was nothing left for her here now, Adam Redmont had seen to that.

Chapter Twelve

She took a deep breath then ran for the cable car. Luckily it wasn't moving fast and she was able to grab onto a handrail and pull herself aboard. She hung on for dear life as the conductor made a great show of clanging the bell, and the cable car inched its way up the hill.

A brisk wind blew through the open car. She shivered in her wool skirt and sweater. She would need a winter coat before long. She had been in the city almost two months now and each day the air grew cooler. The fog was already rolling in from the Gate, bringing with it a chilling winter nip to the air.

Sandy was always reminding her to take a jacket when she left to go job hunting.

"I'd never nag you, dearest, but I'd hate to

see you wind up with the flu, you'd miss all the fun."

What would I have done without her, she reflected, putting her key in the door of her apartment. Already her roommate's infectious good humor had done much to restore her flagging spirits.

Her phone call to Sandy had been met by a delighted reply to come and stay as long as she liked. Sandy's roommate had just gotten married and she hadn't had time to look for another one so there was plenty of room in her two-bedroom apartment for Kit.

When she had told her uncle and Willy what she was going to do and why, they shook their heads sadly but asked surprisingly few questions. They did make her promise to keep in touch and she in turn extracted a promise from them that they would not tell Adam where she was going or how she could be reached.

Now, after a fruitless day of taking her portfolio around to advertising agencies she stood at the window, looking into the darkening street, waiting for Sandy to come home. Even though she was still jobless, it was Sandy's knowledge of San Francisco that allowed her to get into the advertising agencies to begin with. She called countless people on Kit's behalf, persuading them to talk to her and they usually agreed as a favor to Sandy.

Not that they weren't nice and pleasant,

and some gave her portfolio sketches even more than a cursory glance. It was just that there were no openings right now or she hadn't had recent experience or they couldn't afford to pay her enough to live on. Well, she would keep trying.

Sandy came in with a shopping bag in each arm.

"Here, let me take those," Kit said, removing the packages. "Whatever do you have there? We just shopped on Saturday."

Sandy's grin was mischievous. "I thought we would celebrate tonight."

Kit set the bags on the kitchen counter and turned to look at her petite roommate, whose gamin face was all smiles. "Celebrate what?"

"You've been here eight weeks, that's cause enough to celebrate. But, the best news of all is that I heard about a job opening today."

Kit's face brightened. "You did? Where?"

"A firm downtown is looking for a person to do some free-lance artwork for them and I happen to know someone in the office who said she would set up an appointment for you."

"Terrific," Kit said enthusiastically. "Sandy, I don't know what I'd do without you," she added, giving the tiny girl a big hug.

That night they broiled steaks to go with the Caesar salad that Kit made and Sandy's special carrots in orange sauce. In honor of the occasion Sandy produced a bottle of very special wine. Kit watched with a pain in her heart as Sandy opened the same brand of Cabernet Sauvignon that she and Adam had shared that night at the restaurant. They laughed and talked most of the evening, while she tried to hide the memory that kept playing itself again and again in her head.

Adam and her talking over dinner. She listening to his amusing tale of getting lost and finding the restaurant instead of a filling station. On and on the pictures flashed through her brain until she resolutely put a stop to them.

Later, when they were doing the dishes, she said, "I'll need the name of the firm and the address before you go to bed. You get up so early that you'll probably be gone before I have my eyes open."

It was true, Sandy's job at the Pacific Coast Stock Exchange made her an early riser. Kit marveled at how she was able to go to bed so late and still get up before dawn each morning.

"Let's see, I put it in my purse. Here it is," she said, producing a slip of paper.

Kit took it and when she read it the blood drained out of her face. "REDMONT AND SINCLAIR" the card read. She looked up at Sandy, "Oh, no, I can't."

"What's wrong?"

"Redmont is Adam's last name," Kit said. She had told Sandy about Adam and the winery when she first arrived. The other girl had listened, nodded sympathetically and then had told her to forget him and make a fresh start in San Francisco.

"Surely you don't think it's his firm?" Sandy asked.

"I don't know, but I can't take the chance."

"Look, Kit, even if it is his firm, you probably will never run into him if he's up in the Napa Valley busily buying out your uncle. This looks like a good job and I've wrangled an interview for you, why not go anyway?"

"Oh, Sandy, I know you've been working like mad trying to get me in to see people and don't think I'm not grateful, but I simply can't do this, please understand."

Sandy was quiet for a moment and then smiled cheerfully, "Okay, just do me a favor and call them and tell them you're not coming."

"Sandy, you're not angry, are you?"

"Of course not, we'll try again somewhere else. Looks like that torch you're carrying still hasn't burnt out, that's all."

Early the next morning Kit called and cancelled her appointment. Then she took her portfolio, dressed in her best suit and comfortable shoes and began calling on places on her own. Halfway through the day, she found herself walking by the building where her interview would have taken place.

It was a large modern office building with a

street number emblazoned on the front in large gold numerals. She supposed that Redmont and Sinclair occupied one floor of it. She was about to go in and check the directory on the street floor, just out of curiosity, when she heard her name being called. She turned to see Vince striding toward her. She scarcely recognized him because he had exchanged his beachwear for a three piece suit, now looking like a typical San Francisco executive.

"Kit, how great to see you," he said when he reached her.

"Hello, Vince. How are you? or should I ask, how is Teddy?"

"Teddy is fine, just fine. He's home now and we're all growing tired of seeing his scar," Vince laughed.

Kit smiled, not knowing quite what to say. The other person that they had in common was someone she did not want to discuss. Finally, Vince broke the silence.

"What are you doing in San Francisco?"

"Job hunting," she said, raising her portfolio slightly so that he could see it.

Again, there was a moment's pause. He did not bring up the winery or ask her why she had left. Instead he took her arm and said, "Let me buy you lunch. I assume you haven't eaten and I have some time before my next appointment."

"I . . ." she hesitated, unsure whether that

would be wise. He looked so much like Adam that the pain of standing and looking into his gray eyes was almost unbearable.

"Come on, I know a great place around the corner that makes homemade soup," he said.

She was hungry, and what was the harm in having lunch with him? He had never been anything but kind to her. "Okay," she agreed.

Lunch was everything he had promised in the crowded noisy restaurant. Delicious homemade soup with freshly baked sourdough bread served with a flourish. They talked about his children and her move to San Francisco. She told him she had not been able to find a job yet but she was still hopeful.

He listened quietly and then said, "There is a job opening in my firm for a freelancer, why don't you interview for it?"

"I had an interview set for this morning but I couldn't do it. I thought . . ."

"That Adam was part of the firm? Well, he isn't. This is my own business that I own with Caroline's father, George Sinclair. Adam has nothing to do with it. Look, I can understand your not wanting to talk about your personal life or what happened between you and my brother but don't let that stand in the way of a job, Kit."

"Vince, you're very kind and perhaps I was too hasty. But I've already called and cancelled the interview."

"Well let me see what I can do about that

after I get back from my appointment. Where are you staying?"

Without thinking she gave him her address and phone number. Then she remembered Adam and started to explain but he held up his hand.

"This is business information that I will consider confidential, okay?"

"Thank you for being so nice."

"Just good business. We need a good artist at the moment and I have the feeling you might be the one. Kit, I know Sally and the kids would love to see you. Won't you come over to our house for an early supper on Sunday?"

She brightened. Sandy was going to be gone all day Sunday. She would love to see Sally and the kids. What about Adam? she wondered.

He must have seen the question written on her face. "He won't be there, Kit. Promise," he said quietly.

"I'd love to come."

"Good, I have to leave now but I'll have my secretary call you later about the interview and also give you directions to the house."

After they parted Kit decided to abandon her job hunting for the rest of the day to buy some presents for the children. She assumed that Teddy had been getting most of the attention lately and she wanted to let the others know that she hadn't neglected thinking about them.

Later that evening Vince's secretary called and set up an interview for the next day. She also told Kit that while she was in the office she should stop by her desk to pick up a map of how to get to Vince's house.

Sandy was surprised by her change of plans. "What made you do it?"

"I dunno. Vince I guess. I like him," she said. To herself she admitted that she was still crazy about his brother.

Indeed when she went to bed that night she went further and was honest with herself. She had never for one moment since the angry scene that day at the beach house stopped thinking about him. He haunted her dreams night and day. The way he looked that day on the beach, the way he moved when he played catch with his nephews. There was nothing about him that she did not remember.

If she were truly honest with herself she would admit that part of her reason for accepting Vince's invitation for Sunday was that she was hoping that Adam's name would come up. She wanted to find out about him and she dreaded the knowing. He could have been in Europe, back East or anywhere in the country or he could still be with Caroline. Her phone calls home brought no mention of him. She didn't ask about the winery negotiations, either. She had not forgotten. In fact, she had given up trying.

The interview went better than she expected. A balding middle-aged man looked over her portfolio and told her he was impressed with her work. He was apologetic when he told her he couldn't let her know anything definite for a week because he had arranged to interview other applicants.

With a smile and a friendly handshake she thanked him and walked out thinking that she had a good chance to get the job. That evening she wrapped the presents she had purchased for Vince's children. They had liked Adam's stories so much that she had gone to one of the larger San Francisco bookstores and purchased a colorful book for each one of them.

Just before she left on Sunday she stopped for some flowers for Sally as a thank-you gift in return for her hospitality. The drive over to Marin County took her across the Golden Gate Bridge. Today it was overcast, with a stiff breeze blowing in from the Gate. The bridge was deserted except for a few hardy souls braving the wind in heavy parkas.

She had no trouble finding the house, even though it was set back from the street in a wooded area halfway up the road to Mount Tamalpais. As she parked the car and gathered up the presents and flowers Sally came out to meet her. Whatever the other woman knew about her relationship to Adam had not diminished the warmth of her greetings now. She hugged her, exclaiming over the flowers.

The children were equally appreciative when she gave them their gifts. Mandy asked her to sit down right then and read her a story from her book and Kit happily obliged. Teddy, looking fit, had recovered from his surgery and now proudly showed off his scar.

As Kit sat in the spacious living room in the Redmont house she was surprised to see a large framed map of France on the wall. She wandered over to take a look at it. Vince stepped into the room with a glass of wine in each hand.

"I didn't know your family came from France," Kit said, noticing how the Burgundy region was highlighted on the map.

"Redmont is really an Americanized version of Rougemont or Red Mountain," he said. "We have relatives who still live in Burgundy and are winemakers."

Kit turned to stare at him. "I never knew that," she said, suddenly thinking about the way Adam had observed her historical tour talk that day. "A Frenchman originally started Silverado."

"I know, Kit," Vince said and there was something in his voice that made her pause.

"You don't mean that that Frenchman was related to you?" she asked surprised.

"We think so. The records are hard to trace because the Frenchman would be related on our mother's side of the family and he didn't leave any heirs. Adam has been working on this for a long time. He believes that Silverado

226

was the winery started by one of our distant relatives."

"He never told me," she said.

"No, he wouldn't. He has always worked hard for what he wanted. I think he would have thought that telling you that the winery may be part of our family history would be an unfair advantage."

Was that why Adam wanted the winery, because it had been a part of his family? Yet, he never told her. He left her to assume that he was a ruthless businessman taking advantage of her uncle's misfortune. Oh God, could she have been so wrong?

Kit could hardly taste Sally's dinner. She silently agonized over the new revelation about the winery.

"Kit, remember when we had peanut butter and jelly for dinner?" Mike asked.

Mandy giggled.

"I don't remember that," Teddy said.

"You were sick," Mandy said.

"Kit said Uncle Adam was a good cook," Mike added.

Kit glanced at Sally, who was looking as if she was having a hard time following the conversation.

"That night you stayed in the hospital, Teddy, your Uncle Adam and I looked after Mike and Mandy and we all made dinner together," Kit said calmly, while inside her the memory of that night and the laughter they had shared cut into her like a knife.

"I never thanked you for doing that, Kit, you were so wonderful with the children, we all appreciated it," Sally said.

By now Kit knew that she had to say it. Whatever pain came afterwards would be nothing compared to the pain of not knowing.

"It was Adam you know who took charge. I just followed his lead."

Vince and Sally looked across the table at each other not knowing how to respond to her introducing his name into the conversation.

"And he told stories and we played games," Mike said helpfully.

"Will you come with us next summer?" Mandy asked Kit.

"Next summer is a long way off," Vince said. "But we can invite her to come here again to see you."

"Yes, yes," the children said all at once.

"We just bought the house from my partner this past year. The kids love it and can hardly wait to get back up there," Vince told her as the dinner dishes were being cleared.

George Sinclair, Caroline's father, had owned the house. She hadn't known. Was that why Mandy had said Caroline had been up there all the time? Bits and pieces of things she had questioned began to fall into place and the torture continued.

Over dessert Teddy asked the question that Kit knew had been coming all evening.

"Why didn't Uncle Adam come for dinner with Kit?"

Kit decided to take the matter into her own hands. Turning to him she replied, "I live in San Francisco now and your Uncle Adam is . . . somewhere else. We . . ." she stopped, the words stuck in her throat.

"Finish your dessert, son," Vince said quietly.

They stood in the driveway saying goodbye, Kit thanking them for the dinner. Vince and Sally had kept the conversation going after Teddy's question, carefully guiding it away from any more references to Adam.

Now, she could hold back no longer. In the gathering darkness she said softly, "I've made a terrible mistake."

"We all make them, Kit. Most of the time we can go back to set things right," Vince said quietly.

Go back, go back, the words repeated in her brain during the drive home. She began to think about all that Adam had told her about himself. He had tried to get her to trust him that day of their awful argument. She must do something. She loved him. She knew it beyond a shadow of a doubt, she loved him and she had let her experience with Tom destroy everything. She would go back.

The next day she called home and told her uncle she would be driving up for a visit the following weekend. He was delighted that she was coming home, Willy and he missed her. "Why don't you come now instead of waiting for the weekend?" he asked.

There was no reason why she couldn't. Her job status was still unsettled and if she were honest with herself she would have to admit that she hoped, now, that she didn't get one. Living in the city was not what she wanted, she wanted to be with Adam. She wanted to be back in the valley she loved.

She told Sandy that night. Her reaction was pure Sandy.

"Wow!" she said dancing around the room with her. "You're going after him. Good-luck."

"I may be back."

"Fight for him, Kit. He must be worth it."

She packed some of her clothes and drove back to the valley the next day. The harvest was finished, the grapes stripped from the vines, the valley quiet and cool.

She turned up the hill to Silverado, the excitement of being back giving way to apprehension. What if he were so angry with her he wouldn't listen? Or worse yet, what if he accepted her apology but told her that he was in love with Caroline? By the time she reached the top of the hill she was in such a state of nervousness that her palms were damp against the steering wheel. She braked the car to a stop then looked around, surprised that Adam's car was missing.

She had been so sure he would be there. Now she realized that she had been foolish to think that he would stay. He had other business interests to attend to, he might be halfway around the world by now.

"Kit!" Willy said excitedly as she entered the house. "We've missed you so."

"I've missed you, too, Willy, all of you. It's good to be home."

Her uncle came in later. After a joyful greeting the three settled down to talk.

"It looks like the harvest went well," she said dully.

"Yes, the manager that Adam hired is very good. He used to work at a winery in Santa Clara, he brings a lot of experience with him."

"He hired a manager? I don't understand."

"He's gone, honey," her uncle said.

"Gone," she repeated, numbly.

"Not long after you left, he hired the help I needed, then packed his bags and left."

She felt as if the world had come crashing down on her in that moment. He had gone. Had Caroline gone with him? Could she have been so wrong about one person, she had to know, she had to ask.

"Have you sold out to him?"

"Nope. Said he changed his mind. He lent me what I needed to make repairs and hired a manager to help run this place. Said he wasn't ready to exercise his option to buy."

Kit saw a glimmer of hope in what her uncle was telling her. If Adam hadn't bought the winery, the winery that he insisted he was going to have, the winery that probably was started by a member of his own family, there must be a good reason. Could it possibly be that that reason was her? She had to know.

"Where did he go? I've got to see him."

"Well now, you both left in such a hurry I might have gotten my instructions mixed up," her uncle said, grinning broadly. "You told me not to tell him where you were. He left with no instructions except that he would be in touch."

Willy came up and put a hand on his shoulder. "He's at the beach house, honey. We spoke to him two days ago."

The beach house. She wanted to go to him, she wanted to run to her car right now. She looked at the two of them.

Her uncle was studying her face. "Yes, Kit, listen to your heart. You know what you have to do, what you want to do."

She left her suitcase in the hall and flew down the front steps.

The drive to the coast was longer than she remembered and her stomach was twisted in a knot of apprehension as she turned onto the coastal highway. She had told him she hated him so many times that she was not sure he would believe her now when she admitted the truth. In her mind she replayed the conversation that had taken place that day in the bedroom at the beach house. He had asked her for her trust and she had not been able to give it to him. How would he react now when she admitted that she had changed her mind?

Would he believe her? He had told her he pitied her, and she had flown into a rage because she didn't want his affair with Caroline thrown in her face the way Tom's had been. But Tom was dead, gone forever. She had stopped thinking about him the day of her uncle's wedding.

In a moment of anger he had surfaced again in the bedroom and blinded her to what Adam was asking of her, trust. Why was it so very hard to give that to someone to whom she had already given her love?

The coast was clouded by a dense fog as she negotiated the tortuous turns of Highway 1. She knew that she was driving faster than she should be, but she was so eager to see Adam again to tell him of her love for him that she pressed down harder on the accelerator without thinking.

She thought she was close to the turn onto the beach house drive. Leaning over the steering wheel, peering through the gray misting air, she slowed down, scanning the highway. Then she saw the drive and turned the car abruptly.

She could see the house and Adam's car parked in front. As she slowed down, she also caught a glimpse of another car, a red foreign sports car. She braked to a stop in front of the house and rested her forehead against the steering wheel.

Caroline was with him. A searing pain tore through her body. Tears flowing down her cheeks blurred her vision. Caroline. How could she have been so wrong? Everything she now knew about him, everything Vince had told her, made her think her love for him was right. Yet, he still wanted Caroline.

Suddenly the front door opened and the two of them emerged. Quickly she started the car and backed up the driveway. Adam looked up, saw her and began running after her car. He was yelling something that she couldn't hear, gesturing for her to stop.

She couldn't stop, she had to get out of there. Pressing down on the gas pedal she backed the car over the bumpy drive to the highway then swung it around. In her rear view mirror she could see him appearing through the fog, coming after her with great loping strides, still yelling.

She pressed the gas pedal to the floor and the car shot away. She was sobbing, whimpering and moaning his name as she negotiated the turns, her brakes squealing in her attempt to get control of the car. She swerved, narrowly missing the edge of the highway where jagged rocky cliffs pitched out over the angry surf.

Adam and Caroline, Adam and Caroline. The picture of them emerging from the beach house together seared her brain.

"No, no," she moaned aloud, willing the soul destroying image to fade.

Suddenly looming out of the gray mist were two amber lights. They were blocking part of the road. She must slow down, she must. But she was traveling too fast.

The blinking lights reared menacingly up out of the fog-shrouded highway. Desperately she tried to stop. The lights were on top of her. She heard a splintering crash, then knew no more.

Chapter Thirteen

She felt as though she had been submerged in the ocean and now was floating to the surface for air. Gently, in slow motion, she rose toward the light. At last she blinked her eyes open. She was in the hospital, she knew that. There were bandages on her arms. She tried moving her legs. She winced with pain as she flexed her left ankle.

Then, very slowly, she moved her head from side to side. It hurt, but it was more an ache than a sharp pain.

A nurse bustled in.

"You're awake, good. There are some very anxious people waiting to see you again, dear."

"What happened?" she asked, her head still fuzzy.

"No need to worry about that now, is there?" she said brightly, taking Kit's wrist in her hand. Silently she checked her pulse. The nurse turned for a second, then approached with a paper cup in her hand. Kit looked at her warily.

"Nothing but water, my dear. Come now, take a sip."

Gently she pushed the cup to Kit's lips. The cool water trickling down her parched throat was refreshing. She drained the cup. The nurse took it away then busied herself straightening the sheet.

"The doctor will be in shortly to examine you. Just relax for a few minutes."

Kit rested her head against the pillows.

Slowly her memory started coming back; the drive up to the beach house, seeing Adam there with Caroline, careening along the highway in the fog, then flashing lights. She shuddered, now, remembering what had happened.

Dr. Loffer entered. She had known the smiling white-haired man since she was a child.

"Well, Kit, you had everyone worried, but I knew you were a fighter."

"What do you mean?" she looked at him blankly.

He sat down in a chair near her bed. "You crashed your car into a highway barrier. There was a rockslide on Highway 1. The road crew had just finished putting the barrier up when you appeared."

"I remember seeing the lights but after that, nothing."

"You've been unconscious for two days. We had to make sure that you had no internal injuries when you were brought in so we've been doing some tests."

"And?" she asked.

"Except for a slight concussion and some nasty cuts and bruises, you're okay."

She knew him well enough to know there was something he was not telling her.

"Dr. Loffer is something else wrong with me?"

His kindly face peered down at her, soft brown eyes hidden behind thick glasses.

"Kit, I've been patching you up since you were a youngster so don't fly off the handle at me at what I'm going to tell you." He paused, allowing time for his words to sink in. "I was on call here when a tall dark fellow carried you in. You were not a pretty sight and he was reluctant to let go of you. You were moaning a name, his name I found out later. A couple of times over the past few days you've come to long enough to let us know that something was troubling you. You've thrashed around and said things that lead me to believe that you've suffered a trauma besides the trauma of the accident."

What could she say? He was right and he knew it. She nodded silently.

"I've ordered no visitors for a few days so that you can think out whatever it is that's causing you so much pain. I'm doing this because I think you will recover faster physically if you can come to grips with whatever has happened to you emotionally. You need time to mend, child, I want to give you that time. Matt and Willy will understand. I'll keep them up to date every day so that they won't worry."

"Thank you, Dr. Loffer," she whispered.

"Rest now, we'll talk again."

After he left she felt drained. Closing her eyes she drifted off.

Dr. Loffer was back the next morning. He gave her a thorough examination, telling her that she was to have two more days of bed rest before he would let her up. She told him about her ankle. He had it X-rayed then diagnosed a severe sprain and had the nurse tape it up for her.

After he left she began thinking over what had happened. Adam must have followed her in his own car. If he had brought her in to the hospital he must have been right behind her on the highway. Maybe she should have stopped when he ran after her, given him a chance to explain. But instead, she had run.

She realized now that she had been running since she first met him. She ran from him at the airport, she ran again into an engagement with Johnny. When Caroline appeared at the beach house she packed her bags and fled home. She had admitted to herself that she loved him, yet it only took her glimpse of him with Caroline at the door of the beach house to cause her to flee again.

She began to turn over this bit of self-analysis in her mind. The day passed with a quiet, pensive Kit doing some serious thinking about herself.

The next day, feeling stronger, she had the nurse adjust her bed to a full sitting position. Then she asked for a comb and mirror. The face that stared back at her was pale and wan. The green eyes had lost their sparkle and the honey-colored hair was a mass of tangles and snarls. Still, there was a new resolve about her, a desire to sift through all that had happened to discover for herself why she acted as she did.

She ran because she was afraid to commit herself. She ran because she was afraid to get hurt. It wasn't that difficult to admit to herself. The irony was, she reflected, that she had hurt herself more by running than she would have if she had stayed and seen the situation through.

As she thought the matter over that evening she realized that she had built a barrier around herself after Tom. Because impulsive headstrong Kit Carson had taken one risk too many and had gotten hurt in the process, she had swung completely in the other direction and decided to take no more risks at all.

Adam's words came back to her. "I'll never let you go." And he hadn't.

She must talk to him. She would not run

anymore. She told Dr. Loffer the next day that she was ready to see visitors.

Her uncle and Willy were admitted later that morning. She asked for Adam.

The two older people eyed each other thoughtfully. "He stayed until you were out of danger. After he knew you were going to be all right he left," her uncle said, looking at Willy for help.

"Kit, we don't know all that happened but Adam seemed to feel that if you woke up and saw him it would upset you," Willy told her.

He cares, she thought. He still cares.

"Please, where is he? I want to talk to him."

"He's gone to stay with his brother, honey."

She thought for a moment. A hospital bed was not the place to have the kind of discussion she had in mind. She would wait.

"When am I going to get out of here?" she asked.

Her uncle laughed. "Now I know my girl is feeling better."

It seemed as if a lifetime had passed, instead of just a week, when she arrived home. She limped slightly and one arm that had sustained a vicious cut requiring several stitches was still bandaged, but she was healing.

Now she would call Adam. She would talk to him calmly and face whatever he had to tell her. She got no further than the telephone when her uncle stopped her.

"He knows you're home, Kit. He's been

calling me every day that you've been in the hospital. He said he would be driving up tomorrow."

She would be ready. A calm settled within her. That night she had no trouble falling asleep.

After lunch she heard his car stop in front of the house. Her uncle and Willy had strangely disappeared, each murmuring about some errands that must be done.

She met him at the door.

"Should you be standing on that ankle?" he asked, his glance surveying the length of her.

It wasn't quite what she had expected. There was a cool detachment in the gray eyes.

"No, I shouldn't be," she said, motioning him in. She limped into the living room, hesitated, then took a seat on the couch.

He lowered himself into an easy chair. There was silence.

"Adam, I owe you an apology for the way I behaved that day at the beach house."

His face remained impassive. He was not making it easy for her. Well, she hadn't expected it would be.

"I said terrible things to you. You have every right to be angry with me."

His eyes had not stopped surveying every inch of her.

"As for comparing you to Tom, that was not true, you're nothing like he was."

"Are you sure of that, Kitten?" he asked, his face giving no clue to his feelings.

"Yes, I am. What I said was spoken in a moment of anger."

"Is that why you drove back there?" he asked.

"Yes, I wanted to tell you that and something else."

"Go on."

This was hard. He was like a stranger to her all of a sudden. Why didn't he smile or touch her?

"I . . ." she faltered. He wasn't going to help her. She would have to do it herself. Suddenly she didn't care about anything but telling him. "I love you. Oh, Adam, I love you." It was half cry, half whisper but it came from the depths of her soul.

The expression on his face softened and his body seemed to relax. "I thought you would never admit it, my proud Kitten," he said softly.

"You mean you knew?"

"I suspected when you flew into a jealous rage and accused me of inviting my girlfriend up there."

"I was jealous, I admit it. You asked for my trust, well you have it now."

"Do I?" he was standing up and walking over to her.

Gently he pulled her to her feet. But the kiss she wanted did not come.

"I fell in love with a photograph your uncle

showed me long before we met at the airport. I found the real Kit Carson to be even more beautiful than her picture."

"But on the airplane?"

"Honey, I came out here to buy your uncle out and when I heard you tell me about yourself and how much everything meant to you I couldn't tell you right there on the plane who I was and what I was going to do. I thought once you got to know me things would work out."

"And all the time I thought you would do anything to get the winery," she said.

"You were wrong."

"I know that now," she whispered, clinging to him shamelessly, burying her head in his chest.

He held her lightly, his strong arms holding himself away as much as he was holding her to him. She looked into his face questioningly.

"Caroline is Vince's partner's daughter. She came to the airport that day unannounced. When I called her home that night at the beach house it was to tell her father about Teddy. I am polite to her so as not to embarrass Vince."

"I've been such a fool," she murmured.

"Kit, what will happen the next time you see me with another woman? I'm a businessman, not a monk. Will you trust me?"

"Yes, yes I will."

He kissed the tip of her nose, still holding

her away from him as if the feel of her against
him would be too much for him.

"I want to believe you."

"Then do," she cried.

"I'll try," was his quiet reply.

She didn't blame him for being wary of her.
She understood.

"And Tom," he asked. "Do you still hate
him?"

"No, I have no more hate in me. I was as
much to blame as he."

He pulled her into his arms for a fierce
embrace. She trembled at the devastating
impact of the feel of him. Still, he held back
part of himself.

"If you've stopped hating, then you can start
loving," was his muffled reply as his lips met
hers.

When her uncle and Willy arrived back at
the house they were sitting on the couch
together.

"I've invited Adam to stay," she told them.

"For dinner," he added dryly.

"That too," she said.

For the next few days they saw a great deal
of each other. Their relationship was warm,
even loving, but he was different in one re-
spect. The passionate Adam Redmont who
had made her moan her own hungering need
for him was held in check. She would be
patient.

She was in the kitchen one afternoon baking some holiday cookies when the doorbell rang. Willy was visiting her granddaughter and Adam and her uncle were in the winery. Grabbing a dish towel she wiped the dough off her fingers.

Her ankle was considerably better so that she was able to put her full weight on it. She opened the door to find Caroline Sinclair standing on the front porch.

"Adam isn't here right now," Kit said calmly.

"I came to see you, Miss Carson."

Kit ushered her into the living room.

"I see you have recovered from your accident," Caroline said.

"Yes, I am fine now."

"Good, then you can release Adam from his obligation."

"I don't understand."

They were standing in the old-fashioned room a few feet apart. Caroline put her hands on her hips.

"He came here because he felt sorry for you. Surely you knew that," she said coolly.

"And why would he feel sorry for me?"

"Because he was under the mistaken impression that he caused your accident. He felt if he hadn't run after you you wouldn't have driven off so recklessly."

"I see," Kit said. "Was there anything else?"

The other girl seemed surprised at her reaction. Last time she had yielded, this time she stood firm.

"Yes, just one more detail," she said, her eyes shining malevolently. "Adam and I have been lovers for years. What do you suppose we were doing at the beach house that day?"

Kit took a deep breath. "I don't believe for one minute that you and he have the kind of relationship you suggest."

The other girl's eyes narrowed.

"Listen you green-eyed witch, he wants you for one thing and one thing only. How long do you think he'll be around after he gets it?" she spat out.

"Long enough for our sons and daughters to inherit Silverado," Kit replied.

"Adam is mine," she hissed.

"No, Caroline, I'm not," his voice rang out from the doorway.

They both turned in surprise.

"Darling," Caroline said running toward him.

He took her arm and said a few quiet words into her ear. Her face paled.

"Surely you don't mean it?"

"I meant every word," he said.

She straightened, marched from the room, slamming the front door behind her. They stood in the silent living room while her car roared down the driveway.

Kit looked into his face. The icy mask of restraint was gone. A primitive hunger burned in his silvery eyes.

"Kitten," he murmured, reaching for her.

He kissed her hungrily, passionately, molding her body to his. She returned his fiery kisses with equal fervor.

"I had to know," he murmured, caressing her eyelids with his lips. "I had to know you believed me."

"I never doubted you, my darling. Piece by piece I've removed the wall I was hiding behind. It was my own fear of rejection that was making me mistrust you. I was sure that once you knew I was yours you wouldn't want me any more. When my eyes were opened I knew you were telling the truth about Caroline."

"Not want you," he said thickly. "When I saw you lying in the wreckage of your car I thought you were dead. I nearly went crazy until the road crew came along and assured me that you were still alive. I want you, only you. The winery means nothing to me without you. If I can have you it means a great deal."

"Because of your family?"

He pulled back for a moment. "How did you find out about that?"

"From Vince. You were so determined to have it, I never knew why."

"We've both been fools. I should have never let you go. When your uncle wouldn't tell me where you were I went out of my mind. Marry me, Kitten. I can't live without you."

"Yes, oh, yes, my darling Adam."

He drew her back into his arms and kissed her long and hard. She knew she finally had come home.

"Please buy the winery so we can live here forever."

He looked at her, a wicked smile was on his lips. "You only know one of the reasons that I wanted it, Kitten, someday I may tell you the other."

A cold wind blew outside. She could hear the angry sea sweeping against the shore. Everyone had thought they were crazy to honeymoon at the beach in the middle of winter but they both wanted to come here.

The fire crackled in the fireplace, sending out its warmth to embrace their naked bodies lying on a fur rug at the hearth.

She could hear the steady beat of his heart as her head lay nestled in his arms.

"Adam?"

"Hmmm?" he asked, pulling her on top of him.

"What was the other reason you wanted the winery?" she asked, looking down at the silvery eyes reflecting the glinting firelight.

"You ask too many questions," he said as he brought her mouth to his.

But she stopped a few inches from his lips. "The other reason?" she teased.

Suddenly the soft pile fur was beneath her back. He was on top of her, grinning down at her startled expression.

"The other reason was . . ." he punctuated his reply by kissing the rosy peaks of each breast, "that . . .," he kissed the softness of her neck, "I wanted it," he nuzzled her earlobe, "for . . .," he murmured softly into her ear.

She strained against him only half-listening to the answer.

". . . our sons and daughters."

His voice was a ragged whisper. His words mirrored her own hopes as she lost herself in his passionate embrace.

If you enjoyed this book...

...you will enjoy a Special Edition Book Club membership even more.

It will bring you each new title, as soon as it is published every month, delivered right to your door.

15-Day Free Trial Offer

We will send you 6 new Silhouette Special Editions to keep for 15 days absolutely free! If you decide not to keep them, send them back to us, you pay nothing. But if you enjoy them as much as we think you will, keep them and pay the invoice enclosed with your trial shipment. You will then automatically become a member of the Special Edition Book Club and receive 6 more romances every month. There is no minimum number of books to buy and you can cancel at any time.

- - - - **FREE CHARTER MEMBERSHIP COUPON** - - - -

 Silhouette Special Editions, Dept. SESE-1G
120 Brighton Road, Clifton, NJ 07012

Please send me 6 Silhouette Special Editions to keep for 15 days, absolutely free. I understand I am not obligated to join the Silhouette Special Editions Book Club unless I decide to keep them.

Name _____

Address _____

City _____

State _____ Zip _____

This offer expires January 31, 1983

MORE ROMANCE FOR
A SPECIAL WAY TO RELAX

$1.95 each

Silhouette Special Edition

MORE ROMANCE FOR
A SPECIAL WAY TO RELAX

37 ☐ MAGNOLIA MOON Stanford

38 ☐ WEB OF PASSION John

39 ☐ AUTUMN HARVEST Milan

40 ☐ HEARTSTORM Converse

41 ☐ COLLISION COURSE Halston

42 ☐ PROUD VINTAGE Drummond

LOOK FOR *A MATTER OF TIME*
BY BROOKE HASTINGS AVAILABLE IN OCTOBER
AND *THE HEART'S VICTORY* BY NORA ROBERTS
IN NOVEMBER.

SILHOUETTE SPECIAL EDITION, Department SE/2
1230 Avenue of the Americas
New York, NY 10020

Please send me the books I have checked above. I am enclosing $_____
(please add 50¢ to cover postage and handling. NYS and NYC residents
please add appropriate sales tax). Send check or money order—no cash or
C.O.D.'s please. Allow six weeks for delivery.

NAME _____

ADDRESS _____

CITY _____ STATE/ZIP _____

Silhouette Special Edition

Coming Next Month

All She Ever Wanted by Linda Shaw
All Victoria wanted was to maintain the school her mother had run. Then Clifford entered the picture and suddenly she wanted something new—this lawyer whose touch awoke the passion that had slumbered within her.

Summer Magic by Laura Eden
For Alexa Jones this was to be a summer of rest and relaxation. But a vacation in Adam Carlyle's disturbing presence turned her world around and left her longing for only his look, only his touch.

Love's Tender Trial by Maggi Charles
Sparks flew when Fern first met Jonathan Delafield, handsome attorney, but it wasn't until an injury placed him under her care that they learned how deeply their passion could flow, how completely their desire could consume them.

An Independent Wife by Linda Howard
Sallie Baines was determined to keep her freedom. Then fate brought her before the fiery power of Rhy's love—a love that left a woman once hurt basking in passion fulfilled.

Pride's Possession by Jeanne Stephens
Sara was her own woman, making her own way in the world, but Dr. Court Pride had plans to change all that. His caresses tormented her until she had to succumb to his sensuous demands.

Love Has Its Reasons by Olivia Ferrell
Cara's emotions were dormant until Sloan stormed in and awakened the woman inside her. She shivered beneath his touch, gloried in his dazzling gaze, and reveled in her dreams of the future they would share.

15-Day Free Trial Offer
6 Silhouette Romances

6 Silhouette Romances, free for 15 days! We'll send you 6 new Silhouette Romances to keep for 15 days, absolutely free! If you decide not to keep them, send them back to us. You pay nothing.

Free Home Delivery. But if you enjoy them as much as we think you will, keep them by paying the invoice enclosed with your free trial shipment. We'll pay all shipping and handling charges. You get the convenience of Home Delivery and we pay the postage and handling charge each month.

Don't miss a copy. The Silhouette Book Club is the way to make sure you'll be able to receive every new romance we publish before they're sold out. There is no minimum number of books to buy and you can cancel at any time.

This offer expires March 31, 1983

Silhouette Book Club, Dept. SRSE 78
120 Brighton Road, Clifton, NJ 07012

Please send me 6 Silhouette Romances to keep for 15 days, absolutely free. I understand I am not obligated to join the Silhouette Book Club unless I decide to keep them.

NAME

ADDRESS

CITY   STATE   ZIP

READERS' COMMENTS ON SILHOUETTE SPECIAL EDITIONS:

"I just finished reading the first six Silhouette Special Edition Books and I had to take the opportunity to write you and tell you how much I enjoyed them. I enjoyed all the authors in this series. Best wishes on your Silhouette Special Editions line and many thanks."

—B.H.*, Jackson, OH

"The Special Editions are really special and I enjoyed them very much! I am looking forward to next month's books."

—R.M.W.*, Melbourne, FL

"I've just finished reading four of your first six Special Editions and I enjoyed them very much. I like the more sensual detail and longer stories. I will look forward each month to your new Special Editions."

—L.S.*, Visalia, CA

"Silhouette Special Editions are — 1.) Superb! 2.) Great! 3.) Delicious! 4.) Fantastic! . . . Did I leave anything out? These are books that an adult woman can read . . . I love them!"

—H.C.*, Monterey Park, CA

* names available on request